SOVIET
SOCIOLOGY
OF
SCIENCE

SOVIET SOCIOLOGY OF SCIENCE

LINDA L. LUBRANO

School of International Service
The American University
Washington, D.C.

American Association for the
Advancement of Slavic Studies

Columbus, Ohio

1976

SOVIET SOCIOLOGY OF SCIENCE

CONTENTS

PREFACE

In a 1972 issue of *Voprosy istorii estestvoznaniia i tekhniki*, it was noted that there were more than forty organizations and 250 researchers doing work on *naukovedenie* in the Soviet Union.* *Naukovedenie* refers to the systematic study of science from a variety of disciplinary perspectives, one of which is the sociology of science. The following review of recent Soviet literature demonstrates the close relationship between the sociological dimensions of science and the general characteristics of *naukovedenie* in the USSR. Accordingly, the discussion of Soviet sociology of science (Part Two) is preceded by a description of the institutional development of *naukovedenie* as a field of inquiry (Part One).

The essay makes no attempt to assess the work of all specialists and institutes dealing with *naukovedenie*. It focuses upon those publications that are, in my judgment, most representative of the scholarship in Soviet sociology of science during the past several years. My purpose has been to portray the sociological perspective on science as it has developed in the Soviet Union. In so doing I hope that I have not misrepresented any of the ideas or intentions of Soviet scholars in this field.

The Russian word for science, *nauka*, is translated literally as "knowledge" and generally includes the Western conception of social science. Nevertheless, it is clear from the literature under review that the Soviet "study of science" refers mainly to the natural sciences as the object of inquiry, while the social sciences provide the methodological framework of analysis. Consistent with the Soviet conception of *naukovedenie*, my remarks are directed primarily to

---

*G. I. Samoilov, "IV Simpozium po naukovedeniiu i nauchno-tekhnicheskomu prognozirovaniiu," *Voprosy istorii estestvoznaniia i tekhniki*, no. 41 (1972), p. 87.

the natural sciences. Wherever the generalizations in the Soviet literature apply also to the social sciences, the broader meaning of the term will be clear from the context of the discussion.

For easier bibliographical reference, full citation forms are repeated in the footnotes of each section, even if the source was mentioned in an earlier part of the text. The transliteration of Russian names and titles follows the system used by the Library of Congress, except for the elimination of diacritical marks. Proper names ending in ii or yi have been transliterated as y.

The initial suggestion for a survey of the Soviet literature on the sociology of science came from my friend and colleague, Alex Simirenko. I am grateful to him and to the Research and Development Committee of the American Association for the Advancement of Slavic Studies for their support of this work. Data from the sources discussed in the essay are being incorporated into my current study of the career patterns of Soviet and American scientists, which is supported by a grant from the National Science Foundation.

I owe a particular debt of gratitude to Murray Feshbach, who brought many sources to my attention and who generously made available those publications not at the Library of Congress. I want to thank him and Alexander Vucinich for their precise and helpful comments on the manuscript. My appreciation is extended also to Elizabeth Anthony for her excellent research assistance; to Leah White, who patiently typed the manuscript; and to Aaron Greenberg for his criticisms and continual encouragement.

L. L. L.

Part One: *Naukovedenie* in the Soviet Union

The rapid pace of the scientific-technical revolution in the twentieth century has had a profound impact on most aspects of our daily lives. Through a variety of media, analysts have examined the social and economic effects of expanding technology, with its concomitant changes in the international political structure. Natural scientists, science fiction writers, and social scientists have given us forecasts of future transformations in social behavior and morality. One of the many questions raised is whether human beings can create conditions that foster and control scientific progress and its consequences. The relationships between society and contemporary science have become central concerns of many scholars, including those in the Soviet Union.

As a starting point for their discussions of the historical role of science and technology, Soviet social scientists emphasize the tremendous growth of science during the past century. According to one source, two-thirds of all scientific knowledge has been obtained since 1900.[1] The number of people engaged professionally in scientific work increased exponentially, at least until the early 1960s, when two Soviet analysts referred to it as a "mass profession."[2] This term may seem to be an exaggeration, except when we consider the broader Soviet definition of "scientific work," which includes most forms of intellectual labor. Nonetheless, the increase of natural scientists alone has been substantial, as described most dramatically by Derek de Solla Price in *Little Science, Big Science*.[3]

---

[1]P. A. Rachkov, *Naukovedenie: problemy, struktura, elementy* (Moscow, 1974), pp. 4-5.

[2]S. R. Mikulinsky and N. I. Rodny, "Nauka kak predmet spetsial'nogo issledovaniia," *Voprosy filosofii*, no. 5 (1966), p. 26.

[3]Derek de Solla Price, *Little Science, Big Science* (New York: Columbia University Press, 1963).

Price's book is cited frequently in the Soviet literature as an example of the "informational approach" to the
study of science, and he is credited with the role of advancing our understanding of the internal mechanisms of
scientific growth.[4] It is argued, by Price and others, that
the individual scientist can no longer cope with the rapid
expansion of scientific information. This has given rise to
"big science," or the development of collaborative projects
by teams of scientists in large research organizations. The
scale of scientific research has changed, but science cannot
continue to increase at the same pace. S. R. Mikulinsky,
P. A. Rachkov, and others contend, therefore, that science
should be developed "intensively," that is, through a continual improvement of the quality of scientific personnel and
organizations.[5] In order for the government to make effective policies in these areas, it needs to have accurate
assessments of the nature and conditions of scientific progress. In the Soviet Union this need has prompted social
scientists to study the many aspects of scientific activity.

The systematic study of science as a special field of
knowledge is usually traced to the interwar period when rapid
developments in science and technology were becoming more obvious. Soviet authors refer most frequently to the work of
the Russian scholar I. Borichevsky and to the Polish profes-
sor T. Kotarbinski for early studies in the field,[6] although
G. M. Dobrov traces the study of science in the twentieth
century to V. Ostval'd and I. I. Val'den.[7] There were
several terms to describe the "study of science" or "science
of science," and there was no agreement on the methodology
that should be used. The subject was conceived initially
from several disciplinary perspectives, including philosophy,

---

[4]Rachkov, p. 6.

[5]Ibid.

[6]I. Borichevsky, "Naukovedenie kak tochnaia nauka,"
Vestnik znaniia, no. 12 (1926). No direct citation is given
for Kotarbinski's work in 1927. See I. I. Leiman, Nauka kak
sotsial'nyi institut (Leningrad, 1971), p. 33; and Rachkov,
p. 11.

[7]V. Ostval'd, Velikie liudi (1910); P. I. Val'den, Nauka
i zhizn' (1922). Dobrov traces the study of science to
Descartes's observation on the productivity of scientists in
the seventeenth century and to Galton's mathematical approach
to scientific discoveries in the nineteenth century. G. M.
Dobrov, Nauka o nauke, 2d ed. (Kiev, 1970), pp. 9-11.

psychology, sociology, organizational theory, and history. At international congresses on the history and philosophy of science, therefore, the initial difficulties of reaching a common understanding of the term "science" were compounded by disagreements on the best approach for the study of science.

Soviet scholars consider *The Social Function of Science* by J. D. Bernal[8] to be the most influential book on science during this period. In Soviet literature Bernal is called the "pioneer" and "founder" of the "science of science" as a systematic, multidisciplinary study of the nature and regularities of scientific development.[9] His book covers a wide range of issues related to scientific activity. It is considered particularly significant for its elaborate treatment of the question, "What is science and what are its methods?" *The Social Function of Science* combines historical descriptions with evaluations of research efficiency, the training of scientific personnel, the sociology of research organizations, and some of the normative questions regarding the social and political impact of scientific development. Bernal shows how science is one of the decisive factors for our daily and future existence, and he is praised by Soviet sociologists for his suggestion that science be planned and placed in the service of the whole society.[10]

From the Soviet perspective the next major landmarks in the field are *Science Since Babylon*[11] and *Little Science, Big Science*, both by Derek Price. Price was one of the first to introduce statistical methods to the study of scientific behavior. I. I. Leiman and other Soviet scholars feel that he thereby contributed valuable empirical data on science and useful methods of data processing.[12] Another American book mentioned frequently in Soviet literature is *Scientists in*

---

[8]J. D. Bernal, *The Social Function of Science* (New York: Macmillan Company, 1939). Also cited frequently is J. D. Bernal, *Science in History* (New York: Hawthorn Books, Inc., 1954).

[9]Rachkov, p. 12; Gennady Gurgenidze, "Problems of the Science of Science: A Survey," *Social Sciences*, no. 1 (1974), p. 74.

[10]For example, see Leiman, p. 34.

[11]Derek de Solla Price, *Science Since Babylon* (New Haven: Yale University Press, 1961).

[12]Leiman, pp. 35-36.

5

Organizations by Don Pelz and Frank Andrews.[13] The authors
are not given a prominent place in the development of the
study of science, but their ideas and data are often incorporated into Soviet research.

After noting the rapid pace of scientific growth and the
contributions of certain American, British, and Polish
scholars to the "study of science," I. A. Maizel' and other
Soviet writers usually proceed to a discussion of the Marxist
conception of science. Maizel' says that Marxism has had a
decisive impact on "bourgeois sociology," even if it provides
nothing more than a point of departure for the analysis of
relationships between knowledge and social reality.[14] Not
too much attention is given, however, to the specific views
of Marx and Engels on the social role of science, except to
say that they studied science within its social context. A
typical statement is that "the theoretical basis for the
sociology of science consists of the principles of Marxist
general sociological theory--historical materialism--which
presents an understanding of the place of science in
society."[15]

The literature under review is written generally in a
nonpolemical, academic style. The ideological assumptions
are pervasive, however, and can be summarized as follows:
Science is a human activity which takes place within a social
environment that is itself conditioned by the economic forces
of a certain historical period. As a historical phenomenon,
the development of science is considered inseparable from the
evolution of society toward communism. In its broadest meaning, science provides people with a cognitive orientation to
their environment. Through science mankind uncovers the laws
of nature and social change, and with this knowledge it gradually learns to control the surrounding world and its own
future development. Scientific activity, as part of the social environment, is itself controllable, and the results of
scientific research can be directed toward the elevation of
mankind to its highest stage of human development.

---

[13]Donald Pelz and Frank Andrews, *Scientists in Organizations* (New York: John Wiley and Sons, Inc., 1966).
[14]I. A. Maizel', *Sotsiologiia nauki: problemy i perspektivy* (Leningrad, 1974), pp. 16-17.
[15]V. Zh. Kelle and S. R. Mikulinsky, eds., "Vvedenie,"
Sotsiologicheskie problemy nauki (Moscow, 1974), p. 10.

It will become evident during our review of the Soviet
literature on science that these ideological assumptions influence the selection and treatment of research topics and
the practical goals that are sought. The belief that there
are patterns of human behavior amenable to social control has
probably served as a positive impetus to the systematic study
of scientific behavior. This does not mean that Soviet studies of science are unidimensional or standardized in dogma.
On the contrary, the Marxian paradigm provides a philosophical perspective for a wide variety of subjects and opinions.
The different points of view derive largely from the many
disciplinary backgrounds that Soviet science specialists
bring to their work.

It is significant, perhaps, that little use is made of
the work by J. B. Conant, J. Bronowski, Bernard Barber,
Robert Merton, Don Price, and the recent expansion of systematic studies on science in England and the United States.[16]
The most probable reason is the incompatibility between their
theoretical perspectives and the Marxian orientation of Soviet
sociologists of science. For example, Bernard Barber's book
on *Science and the Social Order* emphasizes science's need for
relative autonomy from social control. His analysis is based
on the assumption that a "liberal" social structure is most
congruent with the effective functioning of science. By contrast, an "authoritarian" social structure (such as in the
Soviet Union) is viewed as potentially harmful to scientific
development. Such a perspective on the relationship between
science and society is inimical to the Soviet view that communism provides the best economic and social environment for
science.

Soviet acknowledgment and praise of some of the Western
literature on the sociology and history of science is combined with the criticism or selective neglect of other
studies. The result is a partial vacuum in Soviet research

---

[16]It is clear, however, that Soviet scholars are aware
of the Western literature on science that developed in the
late 1950s. For example, Barber's article on "Resistance by
Scientists to Scientific Discovery," *Science* 134 (1961), is
cited favorably, and a recent article by E. Z. Mirskaia,
"Eticheskie reguliativy funktsionirovaniia nauki," *Voprosy
filosofii*, no. 3 (1975), draws extensively from Merton's work
on the ethos of science. See below, pp. 51-52.

in this area.[17] However, American studies of science suffer from a more general lack of familiarity with work being done in the Soviet Union. It is hoped, therefore, that this essay will encourage a greater awareness and use of the Soviet literature on the sociology of science.

---

[17]Bernard Barber, *Science and the Social Order* (New York: Collier Books, 1962), chap. 3.

I. *Naukovedenie* as a Field of Inquiry

Soviet studies of science were inhibited during the Stalin
period and lay dormant throughout the 1950s. The revival of
Soviet interest in *naukovedenie* can be traced to the work of
A. I. Uemov and M. M. Karpov in 1961,[1] and in the following
year a meeting between G. M. Dobrov and Derek Price appar-
ently contributed to an immediate expansion of Soviet research on scientific information.[2] A significant turning
point, however, was the 1965 International Congress on the
History of Science, where the British scholars J. D. Bernal
and A. L. Mackay delivered a paper called "On the Roads to a
Science of Science," later reprinted in *Voprosy istorii,
estestvoznaniia i tekhniki.*[3]

Bernal and Mackay argued that the prerequisites for a
"science of science" were an adequate quantity of data and
the development of a theoretical framework. Systematic research could then combine statistical analyses of the regularities of scientific development with studies of "critical
events" (crises) in science and could also examine science as
a system of communication and behavior. The authors pro-

---

[1]A. I. Uemov, "Nekotorye tendentsii v razvitii
estestvennykh nauk i printsipy ikh klassifikatsii," *Voprosy
filosofii*, no. 8 (1961), pp. 66-75; M. M. Karpov, *Nauka i
razvitie obshchestva* (Moscow, 1961). See below, p. 30.

[2]At that time (1962) science specialists were preoccu-
pied with mathematical approaches to the exponential growth
of science, and two years later a special department was
formed in the Ukrainian Academy of Sciences to study problems
of information in the history of science. Yakov Rabkine,
Origines et développements de la recherche sur la recherche
en Union Soviétique," *Le Progrès scientifique*, no. 170
(1974), pp. 41-42.

[3]J. D. Bernal and A. L. Mackay, "Na putiakh k nauke o
nauke," *Voprosy istorii estestvoznaniia i tekhniki*, no. 21
(1967), pp. 62-68.

posed, therefore, that a historical survey of available data be followed by the establishment of a classification scheme that would systematize the information into meaningful categories. They suggested, for example, that a typology of discoveries be used to distinguish between single/multiple and accidental/purposeful discoveries.

The authors noted that the science of science was multidisciplinary and should include sociological and social-psychological experimentation on optimum conditions for scientific work. They made a distinction between "pure" and "applied" studies, whereby the former describe and analyze scientific developments and the latter consider the application of science to social needs. Finally, Bernal and Mackay called for the establishment of special academic positions and data-collecting agencies to carry out the above efforts.

The Bernal-Mackay paper provided an impetus to those Soviet scholars who wanted a professional study of contemporary science. A key article on "Science as a Special Subject of Research" was published in the May 1966 issue of *Voprosy filosofii*. The authors, S. R. Mikulinsky and N. I. Rodny, took the lead in advocating the development in the USSR of a special field of inquiry called *naukovedenie*, or the "study of science." This term was translated from the Polish word *naukoznawstwo*, which Mikulinsky and Rodny preferred to *nauka o nauke* or literally "science of science."[4]

The authors defined two key characteristics of *naukovedenie* as it was viewed at the time. One was its origins in, and close ties to, the history of science. They noted that several Western scholars became involved in an analysis of the contemporary problems of science through their initial concern with the history of scientific developments.[5]

---

[4]S. R. Mikulinsky and N. I. Rodny, "Nauka kak predmet spetsial'nogo issledovaniia," *Voprosy filosofii*, no. 5 (1966), p. 26. The term *naukovedenie* was used at least as early as 1926. See p. 3, n. 6.

[5]Robert Merton has suggested, however, that about half of the early studies of science came from natural scientists rather than historians. In his opinion, this resulted in *ad hoc*, speculative treatments of the relationships between science and society, and "a thin scattering of unconnected findings" (p. 10). He shows how the field lacked systematic inquiry, either from a historical or sociological perspec-

10

However, the study of science as a whole required an under-standing of social and economic conditions, as well as the logic and psychology of scientific thought. Hence, the second characteristic of *naukovedenie* was its multidisciplinary nature. Mikulinsky and Rodny emphasized that these various aspects of science should be integrated into an organic whole.

The 1966 article addressed some of the elementary questions that face the formation of any new discipline or scholarly field of inquiry. The authors discussed the need to agree on the definitions of key concepts, such as "scientific growth." They criticized purely quantitative studies of scientific development and set forth their own criteria for measuring and evaluating growth in science. The three indexes they used were scientific discoveries, the testing of existing theories (thereby broadening the application of current knowledge), and the development of new theories. It was argued that the combination of these three criteria provided a quantitative measure for qualitative changes in science,[6] but unfortunately, the problems of definition and measurement were handled too briefly. Without further elaboration, it was difficult to make the transition from their conceptual presentation to the operational level of research.

One month after the *Voprosy filosofii* article, a Soviet-Polish symposium was held in Lvov to consider "the problems of the complex study of scientific development."[7] S. R. Mikulinsky opened the symposium by defining the subject of "this new branch of knowledge" as the functioning of science and its dependence on social conditions. The purpose of such studies, he said, was to provide an objective, theoretical base for the organization, planning, and management of science. G. M. Dobrov added that if the goal of *naukovedenie* was to improve the organization of science, then a combination of quantitative and qualitative methods of analysis was essential. He called for the establishment of specific measures for the different parameters of scientific development and advocated the use of statistical methods in data

---

tive. Robert Merton, "Foreword," in *Science and the Social Order* by Bernard Barber (New York: Collier Books, 1962), pp. 7-20.

[6]Mikulinsky and Rodny, pp. 31-32.

[7]I. A. Maizel' and S. Ia. Plotkin, "Problemy kom-pleksnogo izucheniia razvitiia nauki," *Voprosy istorii estestvoznaniia i tekhniki*, no. 21 (1967), pp. 69-77.

processing. A. A. Zvorykin noted that one form of quantitative measure was the growth of scientific publications. He spoke of using publications to make a "structural analysis" of interrelationships among different scientific fields (presumably through an examination of citation patterns), thereby using quantitative indicators for qualitative changes.[8]

V. V. Nalimov, carrying the quantification of science data a step further, proposed the development of mathematical models to represent relationships among scientific publications, personnel, and appropriations. He suggested, for example, that the following hypotheses could be tested: (1) the rate of growth in scientific publications is proportionate to the achieved level of scientific development, (2) the rate of growth in problems of management is proportionate to the number of objects being managed, and (3) the rate of growth in the labor productivity of scientific workers is inversely proportionate to the number of coworkers in a collective.[9] Again, none of the concepts used in these and other hypotheses is defined sufficiently in the symposium report for us to assess the feasibility of testing the relationships with empirical data.

It is evident that there were some differences of opinion at the symposium regarding the definition of science itself. Some of the participants agreed with Zvorykin's traditional definition of science as a form of knowledge, while others (including Mikulinsky, Maizel', and Sheinin) wanted to amplify this meaning by referring to science also as a special kind of social activity. There was additional disagreement regarding the limitation of *naukovedenie* to the natural or technical sciences. Many of the different points of view that emerged on these other issues reflected the variety of disciplinary backgrounds represented at the meeting. For example, M. G. Iaroshevsky (Doctor of Psychology) tried to persuade his colleagues to consider the psychology of science, while S. V. Shukhardin (Doctor of Technical

---

[8]Ibid., p. 73.

[9]Ibid., p. 72. Nalimov played an important role in the development of a methodological base for the quantitative analysis of science in the USSR. His book *Naukometriia* (Moscow, 1969) received wide distribution among his colleagues and introduced them to some of the Western literature on science as an information system. See Rabkine, p. 45.

Sciences) emphasized the importance of the application of science to production. Nevertheless, the symposium was considered successful in setting forth some of the basic problems of *naukovedenie*, and it stimulated further research in this area.

The different viewpoints that emerged in the 1966 symposium continued to be characteristic of *naukovedenie* in the USSR. There was no standard format for Soviet studies of science, no single set of issues constituting the subject of research, and no unified theory underlying it all. Yet, there was enough of an overlap in the work of individual scholars so that one could see the gradual development of a distinct field of inquiry.

Some problems selected for analysis were more theoretical, corresponding perhaps to Bernal's "pure" science of science, while others were clearly more "applied" in nature. In many cases, the subject matter itself reflected the disciplinary background and goals of the researcher. From the historians and philosophers of science came such topics as the structure of scientific knowledge, the development of scientific ideas, and the historical interactions of different sciences. Social psychologists were more interested in the psychology of discovery and the behavior of scientists in different types of social organizations. While some scholars preferred to deal with the humanistic and normative questions of science and morality or the impact of technology on the quality of life, others emphasized the economic needs of raising labor productivity and management efficiency.

S. R. Mikulinsky, director of the Institute for the History of Natural Science and Technology, USSR Academy of Sciences, and one of the most influential people in the development of *naukovedenie*, has suggested that his colleagues study a wide range of topics at different levels of analysis. These would include, for example, the motives and training of young scientists, their relationships with administrators and technical assistants, and the personal characteristics necessary for scientists to cope with the changing nature of scientific research.[10] Mikulinsky feels that research is

---

[10]S. R. Mikulinsky, "Nekotorye problemy organizatsii nauchnoi deiatel'nosti i ee izucheniia," in *Organizatsiia nauchnoi deiatel'nosti*, ed. E. A. Beliaev et al. (Moscow, 1968), pp. 142-48.

needed on the organization and management of scientific work, methods of forecasting and planning scientific development, and the contribution of science to material production.[11] His most frequently mentioned practical concerns are the establishment of meaningful priorities for the distribution of personnel and material resources among the different branches of science, and the identification of the most significant trends in scientific development.[12] As recently as 1974, however, he stated, "We do not as yet have any objective, strictly scientific criteria for choosing such trends."[13]

As noted earlier, Mikulinsky thinks the field of *naukovedenie* should be comprehensive, with an integration of theory and practice. He wants microlevel research on a scientist's behavior and macrolevel analyses of government science policies.[14] He reminds us periodically that *naukovedenie* was formed in order to establish a theoretical base for the rational planning, organization, and management of science. Its purpose is to increase research efficiency and to ensure an optimum rate of scientific growth in the USSR. D. M. Gvishiani, deputy chairman of the USSR Council of Ministers' State Committee for Science and Technology, and other government officials are in full agreement with the need to collect data on the training, distribution, and productivity of scientific personnel. The government wants to use these data to improve its policies on the allocation of resources and the coordination of scientific activities throughout the country. *Naukovedenie* has therefore received government support, and the scholars in this area have a potentially

---

[11]S. R. Mikulinsky et al., "Filosofsko-sotsiologicheskie problemy nauchno-tekhnicheskoi revoliutsii," in *Nauchno-tekhnicheskaia revoliutsiia i sotsial'nyi progress* by S. Trapeznikov et al. (Moscow, 1972), pp. 34-47.

[12]For example, see S. R. Mikulinsky, "Nauchno-tekhnicheskaia revoliutsiia i problema nauchnykh kadrov," in *Nauchno-tekhnicheskaia revoliutsiia i izmenenie struktury nauchnykh kadrov SSSR*, ed. D. M. Gvishiani et al. (Moscow, 1973), pp. 12-15.

[13]Semyon (*sic*) Mikulinsky, "The Science of Science as a General Theory of the Development of Science," *Social Sciences*, no. 1 (1974), p. 47.

[14]Mikulinsky, "Nauchno-tekhnicheskaia revoliutsiia," pp. 23-24.

significant role to play in the making of science policy.[15]

In his comprehensive view of the subject, Mikulinsky wants the development of a "new" discipline, one that studies the "interaction" (*vzaimodeistvie*) of the various elements that constitute the complex system of science. In a recent article he contrasts this approach with that of Western scholars who try to study science within the frameworks of traditional disciplines.[16] Despite the difficulties of integrating the many aspects of science studies into a theoretical whole, he feels that this is far more reasonable than the artificial dismemberment of the field into previously established and conceptually limited disciplines.

Many Soviet authors agree with Mikulinsky in principle, but most of them confine their work to narrower perspectives. For example, Dobrov accepts the historical base of *naukovedenie* and the need to study science as a whole. But his work tends to emphasize the organization and effectiveness of science within a cybernetic framework. Another scholar, M. B. Mitin, shares the Mikulinsky-Rodny view concerning the need for cooperative efforts among historians, economists, philosophers, and sociologists, but his own preference is for the latter two disciplines.[17] Leiman also agrees that

---

[15]See D. M. Gvishiani, "Osnovnye printsipy nauchnoi politiki SSSR," in *Osnovnye printsipy i obshchie problemy upravleniia naukoi*, ed. D. M. Gvishiani and A. A. Zvorykin (Moscow, 1973), chap. 3; D. M. Gvishiani, "Nauchno-tekhnicheskaia revoliutsiia i problemy nauki," *Nauka i zhizn'*, no. 3 (1971), cited in Gennady Dobrov, "Science Policy and Assessment in the Soviet Union," *International Social Science Journal*, no. 3 (1973), pp. 319-20. Not all of the science studies are policy oriented, however. As mentioned above, Soviet analysts approach the subjects of *naukovedenie* from different disciplinary perspectives. Some analysts adopt a purely academic point of view and seem oblivious to the ultimate application of their theories and data to policy issues.
[16]S. R. Mikulinsky, "Naukovedenie: problemy i issledovaniia 70-kh godov," *Voprosy filosofii*, no. 7 (1975), pp. 40-52.
[17]I. I. Leiman, *Nauka kak sotsial'nyi institut* (Leningrad, 1971), pp. 38-39. For Dobrov's conception of the relationship between *naukovedenie* and the different disciplines, see his diagram in G. M. Dobrov, *Nauka o nauke*, 2d ed. (Kiev, 1970), p. 28.

naukovedenie should be based on (1) the interrelationships
of different scientific fields, technology, and production;
and (2) a systematic collection of data, theoretical generalizations, and practical recommendations for their application.[18] Leiman's definition of *naukovedenie* refers, however,
to the study of science as a special *social* phenomenon, and
he uses a sociological framework for his own research. I. A.
Maizel', one of the many specialists with sociology as a
disciplinary orientation to *naukovedenie*, argues that science
is more than ever a *social* phenomenon and should be studied
as a specific component of social life.[19]

A publication devoted directly to the social aspects of
science is *Sociology of Science* by G. N. Volkov.[20] It examines the sociological problems of scientific change in terms
of the continual interaction between science and society.
Volkov depicts the sociology of science as the most essential
part, the "nucleus," of *naukovedenie*, with its origins in
philosophy and history.[21] He studies the development of
science as a particular form of social reality and sets the
stage for subsequent research on such topics as the direction
of scientific and technical progress, the Soviet system of
science planning and education, and the role of technology in
contemporary society. Volkov's book is cited frequently as
an important impetus to the development of a sociological
perspective on science.

An article by A. A. Zvorykin, "The Elaboration of the
Sociology of Science as a Basis for Its Improved Organization," is a good example of the topics that are characteristic of sociological analyses of science in the Soviet
Union.[22] Although he was not a strong advocate of this approach at the Lvov conference, Zvorykin has worked within

---

[18]Ibid., p. 48.
[19]I. A. Maizel', *Sotsiologiia nauki: problemy i perspektivy* (Leningrad, 1974), p. 12.
[20]G. N. Volkov, *Sotsiologiia nauki. Sotsiologicheskie
ocherki nauchno-tekhnicheskoi deiatel'nosti* (Moscow, 1968).
[21]Ibid., pp. 3-4.
[22]A. A. Zvorykin, "Razrabotka sotsiologii nauki kak
osnova ee luchshei organizatsii," in *Obshchie teoreticheskie
i sotsiologicheskie aspekty razvitiia nauki*, ed. S. R.
Mikulinsky et al., vol. II of *Upravlenie, planirovanie, i
organizatsiia nauchnykh i tekhnicheskikh issledovanii*, ed.
D. M. Gvishiani (Moscow, 1970), pp. 286-96.

a sociological perspective at least since 1967. His conception of the sociology of science includes microlevel studies of a scientist's personality, morality, and social position, as well as macrolevel analyses of the social context of scientific work. Zvorykin considers the organization of scientific research, small group dynamics, the age distribution of scientific personnel, and the information exchange among scientists as some of the main components of this approach. He feels that mathematical modeling and statistical analyses can be used to provide information for the development of policies that will improve the social conditions for scientific development.

Zvorykin views the relationship of science, scientists, and society as a dynamic process of interaction and change. His discussion outlines the impact of science on many aspects of society, such as labor relations and daily living habits, and he examines the effects of social conditions on a scientist's research. He reasons that the development of science depends upon two distinct but closely interrelated factors: the inner logic of scientific theories, and the set of social problems that help define the direction of scientific research. Zvorykin feels that the theoretical and sociological aspects of science must be studied simultaneously, so as to further our understanding of their historical interaction; and, furthermore, he believes the sociology of science can be used to regulate the impact of science on society and vice versa.

If there has not been agreement on the relationships among various components of *naukovedenie*, neither is there unanimity on whether *naukovedenie* should be the umbrella for more narrowly focused disciplinary research. As an alternative, V. V. Kosolapov and A. N. Shcherban' list *naukovedenie* as only one of ten different ways to study scientific activities.[23] They distinguish between other, related approaches, for example, the *naukometricheskii* method, which studies science quantitatively as an information system, and cybernetics, which looks upon science as a dynamic process of information and administration. The information system of science includes the preparation and collection of scientific documents and publications, as well as the communication

---

[23]V. V. Kosolapov and A. N. Shcherban', *Optimizatsiia nauchno-issledovatel'skoi deiatel'nosti* (Kiev, 1971), pp. 32-51.

17

channels through which scientific information is processed. This approach is sometimes combined with the philosophy of science, in order to trace the logical infrastructure of scientific knowledge. Other perspectives include organizational theory, history, sociology, and economics, and Kosolapov and Shcherban' regard each of these as an alternative to the interdisciplinary focus of *naukovedenie*.

We see, therefore, that ten years after the Lvov symposium, the field has not evolved into an organic whole with a common methodological perspective. Mikulinsky's position has had continuing support, however, as exemplified in a 1974 publication by Rachkov, who says that *naukovedenie* includes a variety of orientations which should be integrated into a general theory of science.[24] Rachkov wants to combine the history, sociology, economics, and politics of science with theories of planning, management, and scientific forecasting. He notes the importance of science systems and abstract models of science, quantitative measures of scientific growth and interdependencies, as well as the psychological, ethical, and aesthetic aspects of science. He maintains that all these components of scientific activity should be tied together through a general theory of *naukovedenie*, which is something greater than its individual parts.

In his most recent article on the state of the field, Mikulinsky looks back over the previous ten years and describes them as the formative period for *naukovedenie*. He claims that polemical issues have given way to concrete research on specific areas of scientific activity. The result has been the emergence of *naukovedenie* as an "independent scientific discipline," within which other lines of inquiry (such as the sociology of science) have been strengthened.[25] He notes that the concepts of *naukovedenie* have been modified from their traditional meaning, and efforts are being made to collect empirical data on relationships within the scientific community. The most difficult task that remains is the formulation of a general theory. Mikulinsky may be overstating the extent of agreement among specialists on *naukovedenie*, but he clearly recognizes the logical and empirical complexities inherent in the integration of knowledge into new theoretical systems.

---

[24]P. A. Rachkov, *Naukovedenie: problemy, struktura, elementy* (Moscow, 1974), pp. 18-22.
[25]Mikulinsky, "Naukovedenie," pp. 40-42.

II. Soviet Institutions for Research on *Naukovedenie*

The institutions within which Soviet scholars have conducted research on scientific activities have reflected the changing disciplinary emphasis of their work. Initially the focus was on history and then philosophy; more recently, there has been an expansion of research on the economics, sociology, psychology, and ethics of science. In 1921 a commission of the USSR Academy of Sciences was established at the initiative of V. I. Vernadsky to study the history of science, philosophy, and technology. The following year it was named the Commission on the History of Knowledge, and its members included prominent scholars from various disciplines. In March 1932 this commission became the nucleus of the new Institute for the History of Science and Technology, which continued to place its research emphasis on the history of individual sciences and fields of technology. It also studied the historical development of the USSR Academy of Sciences as the main institution for scientific research.

Six years later the institute was replaced by several commissions, and a special institute for the history of science was not formed until 1945. The Institute for the History of Science, under the USSR Academy of Sciences, was less inclusive than its predecessor, since it did not conduct studies on the history of technology. It was engaged primarily in the history of the natural sciences in Russia, and it printed previously unpublished papers by D. I. Mendeleev, A. M. Butlerov, and others. By 1953 this institute was combined with the Commission on the History of Technology and reorganized into the Institute for the History of Natural Science and Technology of the USSR Academy of Sciences, which has remained the leading research center in this field to the present day.

During its first nine years, the Institute for the History of Natural Science and Technology prepared and published over 330 monographs on the histories of individual sciences and general aspects of scientific and technological development. Its work included a three-volume history of science in Russia, a history of the USSR Academy of Sciences, and a "Classics of Science Series," in which the selected works of prominent scientists were published. Attention was given also to reports from international congresses on the history of science, which Soviet scholars attended after 1956.[1] More recently the institute has expanded its contacts with foreign scholars and is participating in the implementation of the 1972 US-USSR Agreement on Cooperation in Science and Technology.

After 1962 the work of the institute expanded considerably, and it broadened its research into nonhistorical areas of inquiry. In addition to its traditional studies, it began research on the logic of scientific development, relationships within and among science organizations, as well as the sociology and psychology of scientific research. These changes were reflected in the institute's own structure. In 1971 it had eleven sectors and six task groups attached to its main office in Moscow. These included sectors on the Logic of Scientific Progress (under N. I. Rodny), the History and Theory of the Organization of Science (under Iu. M. Sheinin), and Scientific Creativity (under M. G. Iaroshevsky), along with the traditional sectors on individual sciences. Its Leningrad branch had five sectors dealing with such topics as the sociological aspects of scientific progress (under S. A. Kugel') and the history of science institutions (under A. V. Kol'tsov).[2]

The changing focus of the Institute for the History of Natural Science and Technology was reflected also in its series on "*Naukovedenie*: Problems and Analyses," which began in 1968. The institute's first publication was *The Organization of Scientific Activity*, edited by E. A. Beliaev,

---

[1]The preceding description of the institute's historical background is drawn from the *Institute of History of Science and Technology*, issued by the USSR Academy of Sciences (1971), pp. 3-9. The Soviet translation of *tekhnika* in the institute's name is used here ("technology") rather than the literal translation used elsewhere ("technique").

[2]Ibid., pp. 7-42.

20

S. R. Mikulinsky, and Iu. M. Sheinin.[3] Most of the contributors used a descriptive approach to survey the history and
organization of research in the Soviet Union, Eastern Europe,
and the United States. Its underlying theme is that modern
science needs new forms of organization, which are respon-
sive to the massive and rapidly expanding character of scientific research. The following three books in the series
are much more analytical. *Essays on the History and Theory
of Scientific Development* (edited by V. S. Bibler, B. S.
Griaznov, and S. R. Mikulinsky)[4] deals with the relationship
of philosophy and logic to the development of science. The
authors consider the nature of cognition and the methodological contributions of Marxism-Leninism to the understanding
of empirical reality. The philosophy of science thereby
provides the underlying discipline for their analysis of the
structure and evolution of scientific knowledge.

The third and fourth volumes are examples of the institute's research in the psychology and sociology of science.
Scientific Creativity (edited by S. R. Mikulinsky and M. G.
Iaroshevsky)[5] tries to answer some fundamental questions
about the nature of scientific discoveries. It analyzes the
impact of a scientist's motivation, intuition, and social
conditioning on his ability to perceive new ideas in science
and examines the interactions between conscious and subcon-
scious levels of thought in an attempt to describe and explain the complex mechanisms of scientific creativity.
Scientific Discovery and Its Perception (edited by S. R.
Mikulinsky and M. G. Iaroshevsky)[6] approaches some of the

---

[3]E. A. Beliaev, S. R. Mikulinsky, and Iu. M. Sheinin,
eds., *Organizatsiia nauchnoi deiatel'nosti* (Moscow, 1968). A
later book in the series, *Evoliutsiia form organizatsii nauki
v razvitykh kapitalisticheskikh stranakh*, ed. S. M. Gvishiani
and S. R. Mikulinsky (Moscow, 1972), deals with the organization of science in Western Europe, the United States, and Japan.
[4]V. S. Bibler, B. S. Griaznov, and S. R. Mikulinsky,
eds., *Ocherki istorii i teorii razvitiia nauki* (Moscow,
1969). Alexander Vucinich considers this book to be the
most systematic Soviet view on the logical, epistemological,
and methodological attributes of modern science as contrasted
with Newtonian science.
[5]S. R. Mikulinsky and M. G. Iaroshevsky, eds., *Nauchnoe
tvorchestvo* (Moscow, 1969).
[6]S. R. Mikulinsky and M. G. Iaroshevsky, eds., *Nauchnoe
otkrytie i ego vospriiatie* (Moscow, 1971).

same questions, but from the perspective of the social, economic, and ideological factors that are external to the mental process of scientific discovery. Evaluations of new ideas by the scientific community, as well as their social acceptance or resistance, have some impact on the advancement of science. This theme underlies several case studies on specific discoveries and serves as a useful counterpart to the psychology of discovery presented in the third volume.

A special symposium on biographies and the study of creative personalities was held in Moscow in 1972. The result was another publication in the *Naukovedenie* series, *Man of Science* (edited by M. G. Iaroshevsky),[7] which deals primarily with specific methodological issues and research problems encountered in the study of biographies. Rather than the development of general tendencies from quantifiable data, most participants employ the case-study method and contribute informal commentaries on the logical and social conditions of scientific discovery. There is as much emphasis on the "external" situational factors (for example, history and social structure) as on the "internal" personal factors (for example, perception, motivation). This is indicative of the Marxist orientation of Soviet scholars and their concern that creative personalities be studied within the context of their sociohistorical milieu.

Since 1956 the Institute for the History of Natural Science and Technology has published a professional journal called *Voprosy istorii, estestvoznaniia i tekhniki*. It averaged two issues per year until it became a quarterly in 1968. In addition to articles on the history of science and *naukovedenie*, the journal publishes information on the professional activities of the institute's staff, especially their participation in conferences and symposia. It reviews recent publications by Soviet and non-Soviet authors and, although the Marxian perspective prevails, the journal provides an important forum for the presentation of different points of view.

The institute's Leningrad branch[8] published annual

---

[7]M. G. Iaroshevsky, *Chelovek nauki* (Moscow, 1974).
[8]In 1975 the Leningrad branch of the Institute for the History of Natural Science and Technology was merged with the Leningrad sectors of four other institutes into the Institute of Social-Economic Problems, USSR Academy of Sciences. *Vestnik Akademii nauk SSSR*, no. 2 (1975), p. 128.

reports of its conference activities between 1966 and 1970, and since 1971 it has had its own journal, *Nauka i tekhnika*. The journal consists of brief research notes (two to three pages); comments; and reports on the history of scientific establishments in prerevolutionary and Soviet Russia, on sociological and methodological problems of science, and on historical and theoretical questions of specific fields in science and technology.[9]

While the late Iu. S. Meleshchenko was head of the Leningrad sector, his staff prepared a series of books and conference reports on *Problems of the Activity of Scholars and Scientific Collectives*.[10] The first two volumes provided a general introduction to the social and psychological conditions of scientific collectives. The chapters in volume three are divided evenly between discussions of methodological issues and research on the training and distribution of scientific personnel, with special attention given to scientific institutes in Leningrad. The fourth and fifth volumes expand upon the subject of science in Leningrad; and they demonstrate a marked increase of concern with two areas: administration and the social psychology of scientific research, and the methodological problems inherent in the study of the fundamental and technical sciences.

In the January 1972 issue of *Voprosy filosofii*, S. R. Mikulinsky, then director of the institute, described the work of his staff and proposed the following themes for the institute's future research: the contemporary scientific-technical revolution, *naukovedenie*, and a comprehensive history of science and technology.[11] The first topic includes the broad range of philosophical, social, economic, historical, and cultural problems that accompany the processes of rapid scientific and technical change. For example, one of the research groups (under the leadership of S. V. Shukhardin) is studying the evolution of the "man and technology" syndrome, automation, and cybernetics.

---

[9]The 6th issue (1971) and the 8th issue (1973, pts. I and II) were the only ones available to the author.
   [10]G. P. Dzhelomanova, Iu. S. Meleshchenko, and S. A. Kugel', eds., *Problemy deiatel'nosti uchenogo i nauchnykh kollektivov*, vols. I-V (Leningrad, 1968-73).
   [11]"Chlen-korr. AN ASSR S. R. Mikulinsky, zam. direktora Instituta istorii estestvoznaniia i tekhniki AN SSSR," *Voprosy filosofii*, no. 1 (1972), pp. 156-58.

23

In his outline of the second theme, *naukovedenie*, Mikulinsky points again to the need for a unified theory of all the factors that influence scientific development. His emphasis, however, is on the "logic of scientific growth" as the basis upon which interdisciplinary work can proceed. He cites his own work on the methodology of foreign historiography of science and two books by B. M. Kedrov and N. I. Rodny on nineteenth- and twentieth-century conceptions of scientific growth as examples of research in this direction. The institute is also expected to continue its studies on the social, psychological, and organizational aspects of scientific activity. According to Mikulinsky, much work has already been done in the third area, that is, the formation of a comprehensive history of science and technology. He admits that more research is needed, but it is not clear how the separate histories of individual sciences will be integrated.

The Institute for the History of Natural Science and Technology has worked closely with the Institute of Philosophy of the USSR Academy of Sciences. In fact, B. M. Kedrov was the director of both institutes between 1973 and 1974. As early as 1945, a special sector for the Philosophy of Natural Science was formed within the Institute of Philosophy, and the institute's professional journal, *Voprosy filosofii*, included articles on the history and philosophy of science. The general expansion of Soviet literature on sociology was reflected in the pages of *Voprosy filosofii* during the 1960s, and this was soon followed by articles on the sociology of science. As mentioned above, the influential paper on *naukovedenie* by Mikulinsky and Rodny appeared in the May 1966 issue of this journal, and subsequent volumes included the works of other members of the Institute for the History of Natural Science and Technology (for example, S. A. Kugel', M. G. Iaroshevsky, and E. M. Mirsky).

In August 1972, *Voprosy filosofii* opened a new series, called "Man-Science-Technique." The underlying theme of the series was the relationship between man and society, on the one hand, and science and technology, on the other. It was felt that this theme would expose a fundamental ideological difference between "bourgeois" and socialist philosophy. The editors of the journal presented a strong polemic against Western theories regarding the role of man in modern society and accused "bourgeois" theorists of emphasizing only the negative social consequences of scientific and technical

change. The article said that in socialist societies the
relationship between man and technology is a positive one,
especially since modern science provides many new opportunities for human development. It was argued that, by contrast, capitalist systems allow technocrats to use scientific knowledge for the manipulation and repression of hu-
manity.[12]

It was announced that the series would examine ways in
which people could cope with the opportunities and problems
of modern science, that is, with its creative and destructive potentials. The journal invited scholars to submit
essays on such topics as "the social content of scientific-
technical progress," "technology and culture," "creativity,
freedom, and alienation," and "the interdependence of the
natural, social, and technical sciences."[13] The articles
published in 1972 and 1973 covered a variety of subjects,
generally related to the initial theme (the relationships of man, science, and technology), but unfortunately
not integrated among themselves. Contributors discussed the
interrelationships among contemporary science, humanism, and
morality; the environmental problems of modern society; the
impact of technical systems on human behavior; as well as
the problems of psychological compatibility on interplane-
tary flights.

The Institute of Philosophy and the Institute for the
History of Natural Science and Technology, USSR Academy of
Sciences, joined the Institute of Philosophy and Sociology,
Czechoslovakian Academy of Sciences, in the preparation of
a major work on *Man-Science-Technique* in 1973.[14] It is an
attempt to come to grips with the comprehensive nature of
the scientific-technical revolution, defined as "a radical
transformation in the productive forces of contemporary
society being carried out under the advancing role of
science."[15] The scientific-technical revolution is seen as
a process of deep qualitative changes in all aspects of life,

---

[12]"Chelovek-nauka-tekhnika," *Voprosy filosofii*, no. 8
(1972), pp. 29-33.
    [13]"Chelovek-nauka-tekhnika," *Voprosy filosofii*, no. 6
(1972), pp. 184-85.
    [14]A. I. Mogilev, ed., *Chelovek-nauka-tekhnika* (Moscow,
1973).
    [15]Ibid., pp. 352-53.

particularly in the interactions between science and production, science and technique, and labor relations. In addition to an examination of scientific and technical transformations, the authors explore the social-economic and philosophical-ideological ramifications of human development within the context of a rapidly changing social environment. The methods of analysis vary with the broad scope of the subject matter, and the result is a substantial contribution to an understanding of the Soviet theory of the scientific-technical revolution.

In 1974 the Institutes of Philosophy and the History of Natural Science and Technology cooperated on another publication, *Sociological Problems of Science*, edited by V. Zh. Kelle and S. R. Mikulinsky.[16] It was issued as part of the "*Naukovedenie*: Problems and Analyses" series and focused directly on the sociology of science as a disciplinary framework and a subject for academic inquiry. The three parts of the book deal respectively with the general nature of science in its social environment, several problems related to the organization of science, and the behavior of individual scholars in scientific collectives. The contributions vary in theoretical focuses and levels of analysis, each dealing with a major aspect of sociological research on science. N. V. Motroshilova notes, for example, that science can be studied as a part of major social systems, as small group behavior, and as represented by individual scholars.[17] Methodological concerns are combined with the treatment of substantive issues, resulting in a well-balanced and articulate collection of essays.

Another group that has worked closely with researchers at the Institute for the History of Natural Science and Technology is the Sector for the Sociological Problems of Scientific-Technical Progress, at the Institute of Sociological Research in the USSR Academy of Sciences. The leadership of A. A. Zvorykin seems to have placed the emphasis of this sector on the long-term social impact of scientific and technical change, including such problems as forecasting the

---

[16]V. Zh. Kelle and S. R. Mikulinsky, eds., *Sotsiologicheskie problemy nauki* (Moscow, 1974).
[17]N. V. Motroshilova, "Metodologicheskie problemy i urovni issledovaniia nauki i nauchnoi deiatel'nosti," in *Sotsiologicheskie problemy*, op. cit., pp. 30-31.

future needs of scientific manpower. Zvorykin joined D. M.
Gvishiani in the preparation of a four-volume work, *Social-
Economic and Organizational Questions of Science in the
USSR*, published in 1970 by the former Institute of Concrete
Social Research.[18] It was written in response to the 1968
party and government decree that outlined measures for an
improvement of the efficiency and application of scientific
research, and it provided background information for the
European Regional Conference of Ministers responsible for
science policy. Emphasis is on the organizational and administrative problems of science, with some attention given
to the social (and psychological) factors affecting scientific
research. It provides a good overview of Soviet research on
the planning and management of scientific institutions.

The Institute of Sociological Research issued at least
two important publications on *naukovedenie* in 1973. One was
*An Appraisal of the Activities of Scientists, Engineers and
Technical Workers and the Improvement of Their Utilization*,
edited by A. A. Zvorykin and E. I. Kissel'.[19] This volume
is a collection of symposium papers divided into two parts.
The first part deals with the technical and methodological
difficulties of evaluating scientific work, for example,
defining the *criteria* for evaluation, establishing *scales*
of measurement, and selecting the best *methods* of analysis;
and the second discusses ways to improve the utilization of
specialists. Another publication was *The Basic Principles
and General Problems of the Administration of Science* (part
of a series called "Science in the USSR"), edited by D. M.
Gvishiani and A. A. Zvorykin.[20] It is a valuable reference
book for the organization of Soviet science, and is discussed

---

[18]D. M. Gvishiani and A. A. Zvorykin, eds., *Sotsial'no-
ekonomicheskie i organizatsionnye voprosy nauki v SSSR*, vols.
I-IV (Moscow, 1970). The Institute of Concrete Social Research, originally formed from the Department of Applied
Social Research of the Institute of Philosophy in 1968, was
reorganized into the Institute of Sociological Research in
1972.
[19]A. A. Zvorykin and E. I. Kissel', eds., *Otsenka
deiatel'nosti nauchnykh i inzhenerno-tekhnicheskikh
rabotnikov i uluchshenie ikh ispol'zovaniia* (Moscow, 1973).
[20]D. M. Gvishiani and A. A. Zvorykin, eds., *Osnovnye
printsipy i obshchie problemy upravleniia naukoi* (Moscow,
1973).

in the appropriate section below. A companion volume, published in 1975 and called *Questions of Theory and Practice
for the Planning and Organization of Science*,[21] focuses more
upon methods for improving the planning, administration, and
effectiveness of scientific work.

A fourth center for research on scientific activities is
the Sector for Complex Problems of *Naukovedenie*, under the
leadership of G. M. Dobrov, at the Institute of Cybernetics
in the Ukrainian Academy of Sciences in Kiev. Dobrov's
group specializes in quantitative studies of science organization and management. It has tried, for example, to develop
empirical indexes to measure the labor productivity of scientists and the economic effectiveness of scientific work.
Statistical analyses are directed toward the goal of raising
the efficiency and hastening the tempo of scientific development. The most notable characteristic of Dobrov's work,
however, is the treatment of science as an information system, or cybernetic process, which is susceptible to social
control.

One of the most significant books on *naukovedenie* was
Dobrov's *Science of Science*, which quickly became a landmark
in the field.[22] Dobrov tried to measure the interrelationships among scientific fields and the evolution of scientific
knowledge in terms of the exchange, publication, and growth
of scientific information. For example, he developed several
simple formulas to express the relationship between increases
in scientific personnel and the rate of growth in scientific
publications. He also described the relationship between the
existing quantity of published scientific information and the
rate of increases in new knowledge.[23] In *Science of Science*
Dobrov argues that the cybernetic approach is applicable to
the study of science even though its treatment of general
patterns would sometimes ignore the peculiarities of individual behavior.[24] He believes that an understanding of the
complex network of information exchange would enable one to
organize and manage the future development of science.

---

[21]D. M. Gvishiani and A. A. Zvorykin, eds., *Voprosy
teorii i praktiki upravleniia i organizatsii nauki* (Moscow,
1975).
      [22]G. M. Dobrov, *Nauka o nauke* (Kiev, 1966; rev. ed.,
1970).
      [23]Ibid. (1966), pp. 96-98, 136-46.
      [24]Ibid., pp. 168-69.

Since 1969 the Institute of Cybernetics has published a journal called *Naukovedenie i informatika*. Recent issues, edited by Dobrov, indicate an applied orientation and a concern with the economic application of scientific work. Much space is devoted to the methodological and statistical problems of long-term forecasting and to the study of science as an information system. The journal is not the result of current research at the institute, however. Contributions come from specialists in other academy institutes, state committees, and universities, and there is usually a two-year lag in publication.[25]

Along with Kiev, two other cities that played important roles in the early development of *naukovedenie* were Novosibirsk and Rostov-na-Donu. In the mid-1960s the director of the Institute of Mining (in the Siberian Division of the USSR Academy of Sciences), N. A. Chinakal, organized two conferences on the effectiveness of scientific work. The results of the first were published as a book on *The Organization and Effectiveness of Scientific Research* (1965).[26] Papers from the second conference were issued the following year under the title, *Ways of Increasing the Effectiveness of Scientific Labor*,[27] which included contributions from specialists in Moscow, Leningrad, Kiev, and Novosibirsk. Both books deal with problems of the efficiency and application of scientific research, but the vague generalizations of the first are replaced by more detailed analysis in the later volume. There are attempts to quantify and evaluate the work of scientists, including the use of time budgets and statistical measures that might be useful for the planning and organization of science.

Consistent with the practical tone of studies from Novosibirsk is *The Tactics of Science*, written by G. A. Lakhtin at the Institute of Economics and the Organization of Industrial Production.[28] It is a monograph on "applied *naukovedenie*" and describes the daily planning and

[25]The only issues of *Naukovedenie i informatika* available to the author were nos. 10, 11, 12 (1974) and no. 13 (1975).
[26]N. A. Chinakal, ed., *Organizatsiia i effektivnost' nauchnykh issledovanii* (Novosibirsk, 1965).
[27]N. A. Chinakal, ed., *Puti povysheniia effektivnosti nauchnogo truda* (Novosibirsk, 1966).
[28]G. A. Lakhtin, *Taktika nauki* (Novosibirsk, 1969).

organizational problems faced by administrators in scientific
research institutes. More recently, A. I. Shcherbakov, V. V.
Kosolapov, and E. V. Korol' wrote a book on *Science, Scholars
and Their Labor Under Conditions of the Contemporary Scientific-Technical Revolution*,[29] which examines science both as
a system of knowledge and as a form of social behavior,
neither of which is isolated from nor subordinated to production. According to a review by E. A. Beliaev, the authors
try (unsuccessfully) to trace the historical development of
scientific institutions, and they present statistical data
already available from other sources.[30]

Active even earlier in the pursuit of *naukovedenie*, the
Philosophy Faculty of Rostov State University has leaned
more toward the philosophical and sociological aspects of
science. The leader of this group is M. M. Karpov, whose
book on *Science and the Development of Society*[31] served as
an important catalyst for *naukovedenie* in general and for
the sociology of science in particular. As early as 1961,
Karpov addressed the social issues of science and the social
impact of rapid scientific growth. He labeled science "a
complex and many-sided *social* phenomenon," whose development
is influenced by "the needs of material production, *social*-
political policy, *social* structure, [and] forms of *social*
consciousness."[32] Science, in turn, contributes to the expansion of productive forces and has a cumulative impact on
daily life.

Despite the title, a philosophical approach prevails in
a later book on *The Sociology of Science*, edited by M. M.
Karpov and A. V. Potemkin.[33] The first part purports to
study science as a social institution, but actually consists
of a review of non-Soviet literature (especially by Derek
Price and J. D. Bernal) on the "social genesis of science as

---

[29]A. I. Shcherbakov, V. V. Kosolapov, and E. V. Korol',
*Nauka, uchenye i ikh trud v usloviiakh sovremennoi nauchno-
tekhnicheskoi revoliutsii* (Novosibirsk, 1971).
[30]E. A. Beliaev, "Kritika i bibliografiia," *Voprosy
istorii estestvoznaniia i tekniki*, no. 41 (1972), pp. 72-74.
[31]M. M. Karpov, *Nauka i razvitie obshchestva* (Moscow,
1961).
[32]Ibid., pp. 5, 17; italics are added.
[33]M. M. Karpov and A. V. Potemkin, eds., *Sotsiologiia
nauki* (Rostov-na-Donu, 1968).

an object of cognition," the exponential growth of science, and the relationship between science and production. Part two focuses directly upon the nature of scientific cognition and draws heavily from the work of other scholars. Elsewhere[34] Karpov deals with the philosophy of natural science, the laws of scientific development, and scientific creativity.

Some of the other organizations conducting research on *naukovedenie* also tend to specialize in particular aspects of science. For example, there is a considerable body of literature on the economics of science,[35] which is the primary concern of the Leningrad Department of the Economics of Science and Experimental Work, at the All-Union Institute of Problems and Organization of Management (which is attached to the USSR State Committee on Science and Technology). Formed in 1967 and directed by V. S. Sominsky, the department studies the economic effectiveness of scientific-technical progress and the management and control of science in industry. Sominsky's *Economic Problems of Raising the Effectiveness of Scientific Development* and *Measuring the*

---

[34]For example, see M. M. Karpov, *Osnovnye zakonomernosti razvitiia estestvoznaniia* (Rostov-na-Donu, 1963) and M. M. Karpov, ed., *Nauka i nauchnoe tvorchestvo* (Rostov-na-Donu, 1970).

[35]In its focus on the *sociology* of science, this essay has intentionally bypassed the literature on *naukovedenie* that has a primarily economic orientation. Some of the traditional areas of economics that overlap with *naukovedenie* are the studies of national economic potential, the structure of manpower resources, the economic effectiveness of production, and economic planning. The economics of science is a broad field of inquiry that includes such topics as the planning and financing of scientific research, methods of improving the efficiency and application of science, and statistical measures of scientific productivity and development. For an extensive listing of Soviet publications in related fields of economics, between 1967 and 1973, see the "Selected Bibliography of Recent Soviet Monographs," by Murray Feshbach, in U.S. Congress, Joint Economic Committee, *Soviet Economic Outlook*, 93rd Cong., 1st sess. (Washington: U.S. Government Printing Office, 1973), pp. 190-266.

Effectiveness of Scientific-Technical Progress by B. M.
Grinchel' are of particular importance.[36]

By contrast, the Institute of World Economy and International Relations of the USSR Academy of Sciences has examined the international dimensions of *naukovedenie*, including an analysis of science in the United States. See, for
example, *The International Council of Scientific Unions and
the USSR Academy of Sciences* by E. D. Lebedkina[37] and *USA:
Governmental Influence on Scientific-Technical Progress* by
E. A. Lebedeva.[38] Finally the Philosophy Faculty of the
Academy of Social Sciences under the CPSU Central Committee
has focused on the social and ideological ramifications of
scientific development, as in *The Scientific-Technical Revolution and Social Progress*, edited by E. A. Arab-Ogly.[39]

It is clear, then, that *naukovedenie* is a subject of
research in many institutions throughout the Soviet Union.[40]
The Institute for the History of Natural Science and Technology provides the broadest coverage of the field, whereas
some of the other centers tend to be more specialized. There
are cooperative efforts among several research groups and
opportunities for the exchange of information at conferences

---

[36]V. Sominsky and L. Bliakhman et al., *Ekonomicheskie
problemy povysheniia effektivnosti nauchnykh razrabotok*
(Leningrad, 1972); B. M. Grinchel', *Izmerenie effektivnosti
nauchno-tekhnicheskogo progressa* (Moscow, 1974). See also
A. A. Rumiantsev, *Ekonomicheskaia effektivnost' nauchnykh
issledovanii* (Moscow, 1974); and L. S. Bliakhman, ed.,
Voprosy ekonomiki i planirovaniia nauchnykh issledovanii
(Leningrad, 1968). Research on the economics of science is
conducted also at the Institute of Economics in Moscow and at
the Institute of Economics and Organization of Industrial
Production in Novosibirsk, both in the USSR Academy of
Sciences.
[37]E. D. Lebedkina, *Mezhdunarodnyi sovet nauchnykh
soiuzov i Akademiia nauk SSSR* (Moscow, 1974).
[38]E. A. Lebedeva, *SShA: gosudarstvennoe vozdeistvie na
nauchno-tekhnicheskii progress* (Moscow, 1972).
[39]E. A. Arab-Ogly et al., *Nauchno-tekhnicheskaia
revoliutsiia i obshchestvennyi progress* (Moscow, 1969).
See below, pp. 58, 85-86.
[40]In support of this research, courses on *naukovedenie*
have been taught by I. A. Maizel' at Leningrad State University.

and symposia. However, most of Soviet scholarship on *naukovedenie* and the sociology of science takes place within the USSR Academy of Sciences, which provides the most important institutional base for the continuing development of the field.

Part Two: Soviet Sociology of Science

Soviet studies on the sociology of science should be viewed within the context of the foregoing discussion. Most often the sociology of science is defined as the "sociological dimension" of *naukovedenie*, when the latter is broadly conceived. Sometimes it is presented as a better alternative to the multidisciplinary approach of *naukovedenie*. Less frequently, it is defined as synonymous with *naukovedenie*, that is, *the* (social) science of science.

When *naukovedenie* progressed through its formative stages of academic development during the 1960s, it was affected by the level of sociological inquiry occurring in the Soviet Union at the same time. S. A. Kugel', I. I. Leiman, and other scholars writing on the social system of science have been cognizant of changes in Soviet theories of social structure, and a recent publication identifies the sociology of science as part of the discipline of sociology itself. "The *subject* of the sociology of science is the functioning of science as a social institution in the framework of a defined society."[1] In other words, the sociology of science studies the system of social relationships that emerge during the production and application of scientific knowledge, as well as the interaction between science and other social institutions.

As will soon become apparent, Soviet sociology of science covers a wide range of topics and overlaps with other areas of inquiry, such as the philosophy of science, psychology, and management systems. Its distinguishing characteristic is its focus on science as a form of social activity. This activity may be organized in terms of formal institutions and laboratories, or it may be structured through informal patterns of association. The latter in-

---

[1]V. Zh. Kelle and S. R. Mikulinsky, eds., "Vvedenie," *Sotsiologicheskie problemy nauki* (Moscow, 1974), p. 10.

clude channels of communication among those who share respect for a particular scientific leader or who share common scientific concerns. The analysis of science as a form of social activity emphasizes the relationship of science to its social environment. Soviet scholars stress the importance of social conditions for scientific research as well as the social consequences of scientific development.

It is important that the definition of science as a social system be understood in connection with other meanings attributed to the word "science." Accordingly, the first section of Part Two considers some of the problems of definition and the Soviet conception of the relationship between science and technology. This is followed by a focus on the social structure of science itself (section two). Soviet studies concerning the impact of social factors on scientific research have been divided into two parts: those factors that combine with personal characteristics and affect a scientist's creativity, and those aspects of science management that are directed toward improvements in productivity (sections three and four, respectively). The final section reviews the Soviet perspective on the social impact of scientific and technical change.

I. Definitions of Science

The differences among Soviet scholars concerning the focus and methods of *naukovedenie* may be attributed, in part, to the lack of a standard definition of "science."

> Science can be regarded as an institution, as a method, as an accumulation of traditions of knowledge, as an important factor for the maintenance and development of production, as one of the strongest factors formulating the belief[s] and relationship[s] between man and the world.[1]

Science is sometimes referred to as a means of perceiving the world; a result of collective human activity; a product of complex organizational, economic, and social processes; and a historical process. A variety of meanings pervades the Soviet literature on *naukovedenie* and makes a precise treatment of the subject more difficult.

It is possible, however, to delineate three general ways in which the term "science" is used. The first is the traditional definition of science as an accumulation of knowledge, which includes the acquisition and systematization of information, as well as the logical patterns of scientific thought. Second, science is viewed as a system of social behavior wherein scientists interact with their surrounding social environment. The third definition refers to science as a productive force, contributing to the material-technical base of communism. In each case, science is described as a process rather than as a static condition. The emphasis is on the *development* of human knowledge, or the social *activity* of scientists. The dynamic qualities of science are evident also when it is a productive force, since, according to

---

[1] I. A. Maizel', *Nauka, avtomatizatsiia, obshchestvo* (Leningrad, 1972), p. 26.

36

Marxian theory, the productive forces are continually moving society forward.

In some of the literature under review, science is defined explicitly at the beginning of the analysis. In other cases, the author's orientation is evident from the context of his discussion. Sociologists of science tend to prefer the second meaning of the term (a system of social behavior), but they take into consideration the ways in which the social activity of scientists results in knowledge or in an expansion of productive forces. In his book *Science, Automation, and Society*, for example, I. A. Maizel' reviews a series of definitions and concludes that in the majority of cases science is looked upon as a form of knowledge and perception.[2] Therefore, although he uses a sociological orientation in his own work, he acknowledges the importance of science as "a system of developing *knowledge* which is obtained through proper methods of perception and which is expressed in precise concepts, the truth of which is verified and demonstrated by social practice."[3]

Although some Soviet scholars distinguish natural from social science and others refer to material *and* social relationships, in both cases science is being treated as a system of knowledge. The Soviet conception of science, as knowledge, is tied closely to the Marxian theory of the relationships between human beings and nature. Nature does not determine all human activities, but it puts certain limitations on them. Primitive people were victims of nature to the extent that they did not know how to overcome these limitations. In comparison with people of the twentieth century, they derived relatively little from the environment, and their activities did not make significant changes in the physical surroundings.

Gradually, they began to cultivate the fields and to learn the skills for an agricultural economy. According to Marx and Engels, changes in productive forces led to adjustments in social and political relationships. Meanwhile, people became more educated, began to understand some of the forces of nature, and tried to manipulate them. As science

---

[2] Ibid., p. 30.
[3] Ibid., p. 33. Maizel' attributes this definition to the Institute for the History of Natural Science and Technology. The emphasis is added.

37

and technology were developed, human influence over nature expanded tremendously. Marxism-Leninism postulates, therefore, that the key to human control over nature is science, that is, knowledge of the laws of social development and the physical environment. Through modern science, people are no longer victims of nature to the same extent that they were in primitive societies. However, according to Marx, human beings will not attain freedom until they have full rational control over the forces of nature, and, theoretically, this level of knowledge will be reached during the stage of communism.

As a system of knowledge, science consists of concepts, hypotheses, laws, and theories which are developed according to certain principles and methods. In his book *Naukovedenie*, P. A. Rachkov provides a standard description of the scientific process. He maintains that an understanding of the inner logic and specific laws of science is necessary as part of one's consciousness of the material world. Scientific laws reveal the underlying mechanisms of scientific progress and the connections between general theories and observable facts. Rachkov and others acknowledge the argument of Thomas Kuhn regarding the paradigm shift that occurs when there is an incompatibility between established theories and empirical observations. At the same time, Soviet writers emphasize the importance of social conditions and the historical context of scientific development.[4]

The differentiation and integration of knowledge are considered by several authors to be characteristic of scientific development. I. I. Leiman, for example, describes the differentiation of knowledge as a complex and inevitable result of the rapid expansion of science in the twentieth century. The differentiation of scientific disciplines and methods coincides with a specialization of labor, which could have the negative effect of compartmentalizing knowledge, except that the specialized fields actually overlap each other in varying degrees.[5] According to Mikulinsky, Iaroshevsky, and others, there is a reintegration of science in many areas

---

[4]P. A. Rachkov, *Naukovedenie: problemy, struktura, elementy* (Moscow, 1974), pp. 49-51. See Thomas Kuhn, *The Structure of Scientific Revolutions* (Chicago: University of Chicago Press, 1962).
[5]I. I. Leiman, *Nauka kak sotsial'nyi institut* (Leningrad, 1971), pp. 91-94.

and a need for scientists to by psychologically prepared to make the necessary transitions among fields.[6] This has become a practical concern for *naukovedenie* specialists, who are now studying the problems of requalification and professional-field mobility among scientists.

A strong proponent of the view of science as a system of knowledge is B. M. Kedrov. In his article "Regarding the Laws of the Development of Science," he emphasizes the importance of understanding the laws of nature and social change. Such knowledge is considered necessary in order to forecast and plan for future developments in science. Kedrov contends that the laws of nature have their own inner logic, and scientific progress at each stage of history is determined by the cognitive material that science has already accumulated. The "inner logic" of scientific development refers to an overall pattern of scientific cognition, which to a certain extent is "relatively independent." Kedrov points out, nevertheless, that the logical aspects of science are closely intertwined with material stimuli, that is, with the social and economic conditions of a particular historical period.[7]

In an earlier publication, "Paths of Scientific and Technical Development," Kedrov divides the history of science and technology into three periods. The first is the precapitalist period, when technology was only partly dependent on science; the second is the period of capitalism, when natural science was subservient to the needs of technology, yet necessary for its development; and the midtwentieth century represents the beginning of the third period when science moves ahead of technology and opens new possibilities for technical progress. In this phase the central problem is the planning and management of current and future scientific development.[8]

The historical interaction between scientific knowledge, social conditions, and technical needs has received the

[6]S. R. Mikulinsky and M. G. Iaroshevsky, "Psikhologiia nauchnogo tvorchestva i naukovedenie," in *Nauchnoe tvorchestvo* (Moscow, 1969), p. 17.

[7]Bonifati Kedrov, "Regarding the Laws of the Development of Science," *Social Sciences*, no. 1 (1974), pp. 26, 30-31, 34.

[8]B. M. Kedrov, "Puti razvitiia nauki i tekhniki," *Voprosy istorii estestvoznaniia i tekhniki*, nos. 36-37 (1971-72), pp. 3-7.

attention of many Soviet scholars, including N. N. Semenov, A. A. Zvorykin, and others.[9] There is general agreement that science is a dynamic, self-productive, and self-regulating system of knowledge, which functions according to its own internal logic. It is always viewed, however, within the context of its social-historical environment, best summarized in a frequently quoted comment by Mikulinsky and Rodny that science is "not only the sum of knowledge, as they say, the totality of the fruits of the tree of knowledge, but also the tree itself on which they grow."[10]

Sociologists,[11] such as Leiman and Maizel', focus on those aspects of the environment of science that affect the activity of people as social beings and thereby relate the logical development of scientific knowledge to its behavioral components. Leiman introduces his book on *Science as a Social Institution* with a brief discussion of the two aspects of science. He agrees that science is the systematization of knowledge about the objective laws of nature, society, and thought, and that it is formulated in terms of concepts, hypotheses, laws, and theories; but he is critical of those who consider science as limited to the acquisition and dissemination of scientific knowledge. Leiman contends that they fail to see the behavior system through which scientific information is collected, transmitted, and preserved; and prefers to describe science as a form of social consciousness which is exhibited through a particular type of labor.[12] In other words, it is a process of interaction between scientists and their social environment.

Rachkov also deals with the interrelationships between the logical and social aspects of science. Unfortunately, he does not always maintain a clear distinction between his definitions and generalizations. For example, he *defines* science as a system of knowledge, but he says also that the *object* of science is knowledge.[13] Thus, knowledge is both a

---

[9]The views of Semenov and Zvorykin are discussed below, pp. 86-87 and 83-84, respectively.

[10]S. R. Mikulinsky and N. I. Rodny, "Nauka kak predmet spetsial'nogo issledovaniia," *Voprosy filosofii*, no. 5 (1966), p. 26.

[11]References to certain Soviet scholars as "sociologists" are based on the nature and substance of their publications.

[12]Leiman, pp. 9-12.

[13]Rachkov, pp. 24-27.

40

defining characteristic and a goal of science. Given the context of his argument, Rachkov does not mean to imply "science for the sake of science." His analysis becomes more cogent if we turn to his second definition of science, namely a form of social activity, including the whole system of relationships between scientists and their institutions.[14] His two definitions are compatible only if we combine them to mean that science is a behavioral system that has as its goal the acquisition of knowledge.

Rachkov includes a third dimension in his definitions of science. In addition to science as a system of knowledge and a social division of labor, he asserts that science is a direct productive force and emphasizes that it is only through the *application* of the theoretical knowledge obtained through the social system of science that the practical effects of science can be felt:

> Science shows people how to do what they want to do and this is its most important characteristic. If science cannot reveal the rational paths to the resolution of practical problems, then it is not able to answer the demands which its developments have given rise to. Thus every science . . . must be not only a system of knowledge explaining the world, but [also] the means and method for its change and transformation.[15]

Although presented as a third aspect of science, the "productive force" dimension is treated by Rachkov more as a function, or consequence, of scientific activity.[16] We can incorporate this with the first two dimensions and define science as a behavioral system that has as its goal the acquisition and application of knowledge. While the terminology may differ, this definition would probably hold for most of the literature under discussion.

M. G. Iaroshevsky takes a somewhat different approach by defining science in terms of the following dimensions: objective logic, sociology, and psychology. He maintains that the concept of science is interdisciplinary in essence and a special language (terminology) must be developed to express

---

[14]Ibid., pp. 33-35.
[15]Ibid., p. 29.
[16]Ibid., pp. 36-39.

its three-dimensional character. His analysis implies a
certain hierarchy among the components, with the inner logic
of science as the most important. He contends that scientific principles, categories, and methods constitute the
central core of science. Scientific ideas retain their own
value in the face of changes in social conditions, but science is not autonomous. It is a product of the collective
activity of people and, in this sense, it is a "socially-
determined system."[17] At this point, he seems to be using
the social dimension of science as a secondary characteristic, rather than as part of the definition itself.

In treating the psychological dimension, Iaroshevsky
begins with the assumption that the development of scientific
ideas occurs in people's minds. The individual is the most
important "agent" of scientific change and therefore his
perception, motivation, style, and other personal characteristics must be considered essential to science.[18] Here
again Iaroshevsky has identified factors that contribute to
scientific knowledge and to our understanding of it, but the
psychological components seem to be on the same secondary
level as the social ones. Nevertheless, he gives his greatest attention to four "social-psychological problems" of
science: the adjustment of individuals to large research organizations, the performance of assistantship tasks by
highly qualified scientific personnel, the adjustment of
young scientists to interdisciplinary research, and the
scholarly evaluation of scientific work.[19]

One of the reasons why Iaroshevsky may not have treated
science as a productive force is his primary concern with
scientific creativity. Creativity in scientific research is
at the other end of the science-production cycle. Soviet
authorities have had considerable difficulty in bridging the
gap between science and production, and they often speak of
the problems of *vnedrenie*, that is, introducing the results
of scientific research into the national economy. It is
recognized, of course, that creativity is essential to the

---

[17]M. G. Iaroshevsky, "Trekhaspektnost' nauki i problemy
nauchnoi shkoly," in *Sotsial'no-psikhologicheskie problemy
nauki* (Moscow, 1973), pp. 174-77.
[18]Ibid., pp. 178-79.
[19]M. G. Iaroshevsky, "Predislovie," *Sotsial'no-psikhologicheskie problemy*, op. cit., pp. 10-16.

advancement of scientific and technical knowledge, without which production would suffer. But the *utility* of new ideas is a critical factor. The evaluation of science as a "productive force" within Marxist-Leninist ideology emphasizes the Soviet concern with the practical application of scientific knowledge.

Lenin maintained that mind is a reflection of matter and human knowledge is simply a reflection of, or an awareness of, the objective material world. Changes in the material environment are themselves a result of developments within the economic base, which consists of productive forces and their corresponding modes of production. In 1951-52, S. G. Strumilin renewed a philosophical debate of the 1920s when he questioned whether science merely reflected the economic base or actually changed it.[20] If scientific progress led to economic change, did this reverse the traditional relationship between superstructure and base, or should science be redefined as a productive force?

The transformation of science into a direct productive force was a subject of considerable discussion throughout the 1960s, and there is still a variety of views as to the precise nature of this process.[21] The 1969 Program of the CPSU asserted that science would become a productive force, in full measure, only under communism.[22] N. Frolov tried to clarify the ideological position of science in 1963 by noting that the transformation of science into a productive force was a gradual process which, according to Marx, began under capitalism.

> Since the development of capitalism, the role of science has grown as an independent factor in the development of production. . . . [But] the transformation of science into a productive force *in*

---

[20]I. G. Kurakov, *Nauka, tekhnika i voprosy stroitel'stva kommunizma*, trans. Carin Dedijer (Oxford: Pergamon Press, 1966), p. vii; *Soviets Take a New Look at Science* (Stockholm, 1964), p. 2.

[21]See Julian Cooper, "The Scientific and Technical Revolution in Soviet Theory" (Paper prepared for the Conference on Technology and Communist Culture, August 1975), pp. 18-20.

[22]*Programme of the Communist Party of the Soviet Union*, (Moscow, 1961), p. 61.

full measure assumes a much higher level of science compared to its current status.[23]

Despite this qualification, more recent analyses by sociologists have referred to science as though it were a full productive force in the present stage of building the material-technical base of communism.

Science becomes an active factor in the development of those technological processes that will allow people to make maximum use of the forces and resources of nature. Rachkov calls this the "practical-effective" function of science, in contrast to the "knowledge-gathering" and "cultural-educational" functions of science.

The practical-effective function is related to the fact that science is the most important condition for the development of contemporary production and the system of social relations, i.e., it plays the role of a direct force of material production, economic and social-political relationships. At present this function is doubtlessly the most essential . . . [since] it defines the degree and character of the development of the other functions of science and their basic direction.[24]

Rachkov argues, furthermore, that modern technology has actually become dependent upon the efficient and rapid utilization of science.

B. M. Kedrov looks at another aspect of the science-production relationship.

To reveal the fundamental law of the development of natural science means, first and foremost, establishing the material causes . . . that its development is condition by. *In the long run*, science is begotten and advances because of the requirements of technology and production. It is the

---

[23]N. Frolov, "Stroitel'stvo kommunizma i protsess prevrashcheniia nauki v neposredstvennuiu proizvoditel'nuiu silu," *Kommunist Moldavii*, no. 1 (1963), p. 20. The emphasis is added.
[24]Rachkov, p. 48.

practice of social production that sets science definite tasks, in accomplishing which science moves ahead, discovers new laws of Nature and makes it possible for those laws to be practically utilised in the interests of society. It is when a technological need emerges that [it is necessary] to acquire the appropriate scientific knowledge so as to meet that need.[25]

Kedrov claims that this is true even during the current, mature stage of science, since production acts as a "spur" to scientific development. He then cites several historical examples to demonstrate how practical needs have given rise to scientific change.[26] The argument is not completely convincing, however, since it can also be said that people were not conscious of their social "needs" until after the means for satisfying them were discovered or invented by scientists.

Discussions of the historical interaction between science and production usually refer to the development of new ideas and their practical application. The relationship between science as a search for knowledge and science as a productive force becomes evident when viewed in this context. Yet, the acquisition and application of knowledge takes place within a social environment and is the result of the activities of scientists as human and social beings. Soviet sociologists of science rely most heavily, therefore, on the analysis of science as a system of social behavior.

---

[25]Kedrov, "Regarding the Laws," p. 28. Trans. *Social Sciences*. The emphasis is added.
[26]Ibid., p. 29.

II. The Social System of Science

In 1968 S. A. Kugel' wrote a monograph called *A New Perspective in the Study of Society's Social Structure*,[1] in which he refers to the development of a general theory of social structure as one of the most important prerequisites for the scientific management of society. He considers the regularities of scientific development as part of the overall system of societal relationships, institutions, and ideas. The establishment of complex models of social structure can contribute, therefore, to a better understanding of the role of science in relation to society as a whole. Elsewhere Kugel' divides the subject into two parts: the interaction between scientists and society, and the social relationships among scientists themselves.[2] We can follow this distinction by looking, first, at the general sociological concepts employed by Kugel' and Leiman, and second, at the norms of behavior among scientists, with particular attention to the formal and informal scientific collectives that have developed.

As his starting point for a general theory of society, Kugel' deals with the Marxian concept of "class." He compares the advances in Soviet sociological theory between 1966 and 1968 with the early 1950s. The traditional emphasis of Soviet sociologists had been on three basic elements of social structure in the USSR: the working class, the collective farm peasantry, and the intelligentsia. Each of these was treated as an entire social unit (two classes and and one stratum); therefore the relationships between

---

[1] S. A. Kugel', *Novoe v izuchenii sotsial'noi struktury obshchestva* (Leningrad, 1968).
[2] S. A. Kugel' and E. M. Sidorova, "Predislovie," *Nauchno-tekhnicheskaia revoliutsiia i izmenenie struktury nauchnykh kadrov SSSR*, ed. D. M. Gvishiani et al. (Moscow, 1973), p. 5.

scientific-technical progress and changes within these societal groups were generally ignored. Research on intraclass differences developed by the end of the 1950s, and the more recent orientation of Soviet sociologists is reflected in the work of Kugel'.

Kugel' divides the labor structure into "socioprofessional groups," such as manual workers, technicians, and scientists. In his distinction between socioprofessional groups and class divisions, he maintains that the defining characteristic of the socioprofessional structure is the nature of the work, specifically its complexity and degree of creativity,[3] whereas classes are defined in terms of their relationship to the means of production. Differences in professional fields are tied to differences in qualifications and education which, in turn, may be based on class differences, but the two types of social division do not necessarily correspond. In other words, he retains the Marxian concept of class while using a different term to describe the division of society into occupational groups. He can then look at distinctions (and conflicts) within these groups, as well as the mobility between them, without violating the precepts of Marxism-Leninism.

Kugel' is actually superimposing an alternative view of social structure upon the Marxian one. He justifies this approach by noting that a study of the "socioprofessional grouping of the population" has practical significance for scientific progress and national economic growth. According to the class division of society and the distinction between mental and physical labor, scientists are part of the stratum of intelligentsia. But as a professional group, they can be analyzed in greater detail, that is, in terms of their social origins, the quality of their work, and their educational training. Kugel' advocates that more studies be made on the family and regional backgrounds of scientists, especially since the education and skills that a scientist receives are basic factors in the acquisition of a certain type of work, which in turn affects his subsequent social status.[4]

Kugel' considers the scientific-technical revolution to be the most significant influence on contemporary social structure. It has promoted a general increase in social mobility and has changed the social relationships among

---

[3]Kugel', *Novoe v izuchenii*, p. 17.
[4]Ibid., pp. 33-38.

professional groups. From this perspective, he presents a preliminary discussion of the mobility of scientific workers, which is the subject of further analysis in his later publications. Kugel's monograph thereby serves as a useful introduction to the kinds of research questions he considers important, and it represents a serious attempt to place the study of scientists within the context of a general theory of social structure.

I. I. Leiman takes a much more dynamic approach to the study of science and society. Consistent with Western social theorists, Leiman views society as a macrosystem divided into a complex set of subsystems, each of which possesses its own characteristics. The totality of these functionally distinct, but interrelated, elements constitutes the dynamic and complex inner structure of society. Leiman contends that when science is studied as a social system, it is easier to see its interrelationships with the other aspects of society (such as management, production, cultural systems, and so forth).[5] Science is defined, then, as a "social institution," which is "a collection of people organized for the attainment of general goals."[6] The activities of the members of the collective must be regulated so as to enhance the integration of individual goals, to guarantee the institution's inner unity, and to ensure the fulfillment of certain functions for the system as a whole.

According to Leiman, systems can be classified as "open," "closed," or "isolated," depending on their relationship with the environment. He says that the third type is an abstraction and that, in fact, all systems interact with their environment, either "openly" through the exchange of energy, matter, and information, or as a "closed" system through only one of these channels.[7] He does not elaborate, however, on the operational meaning of the "energy" and "matter" interchange. Leiman contends that social institutions are open systems which are constantly influencing and being influenced by their surrounding environments, and science as a social institution, therefore, has the charac-

[5]I. I. Leiman, *Nauka kak sotsial'nyi institut* (Leningrad, 1971), pp. 15-17.
[6]Ibid., p. 19. Although the literal translation is "social institute," Leiman's use of the term is closer to the Western conception of "social institution."
[7]Ibid., p. 16.

teristics of a subsystem interacting with its entire social milieu.

Leiman's broad theoretical perspective is not typical of the Soviet literature on the sociology of science. More frequent attention is given to the patterns of behavior that characterize relationships among scientists, that is, the internal characteristics of the scientific system itself. Leiman analyzes the inner dynamics of science in terms of the characteristics that he ascribes to all social institutions: a functional specificity of parts, a hierarchical structure of interaction, a socially significant function, a set of norms and values, a formally dilineated management group, and material support for the responsible operation of the system. Every social institution possesses a central core of activities and is directed toward the achievement of a corresponding goal. In the case of science, its "essential organic elements" are the ideas, hypotheses, and facts of science together with the scientists and the methodology they use. The basic goal of scientific activity is knowledge of the laws of objective reality for the satisfaction of social needs.[8]

The internal dynamics of scientific systems are given greater attention in *The Sociological Problems of Science*. A. Titmonas and other contributors to this volume consider the viability of science as a quasi-independent institution. "Science is not simply an integral element of society as a system, but [it is] a complex and self-regulating subsystem --a relatively independent social organism."[9] The institutionalization of science is described as a dialectical process whereby science becomes independent from nonscientific social formations, while simultaneously intensifying its relationships with society. The social system of science encompasses other social institutions, such as universities, academies, and so forth. These organizational forms are necessary for the institutionalization of science and must be accompanied by a growth in professionalism, that is, the development of traditions, values, and orientations among the scientists themselves.[10]

---

[8]Ibid., pp. 20-24.
[9]A. Titmonas, "K voprosy o predposylkakh institutsionalizatsii nauki," in *Sotsiologicheskie problemy nauki*, ed. V. Zh. Kelle and S. R. Mikulinsky (Moscow, 1974), pp. 160-61.
[10]Ibid., pp. 163, 167.

The values and orientations that characterize scientific research and the professional interactions of scientists are generally referred to as the ethos of science. A form of scientific ethos is discussed by several Soviet scientists, including those cited in P. T. Prikhod'ko's *Roads Into Science*. K. I. Skriabin, for example, says that the specialist should be characterized by a selfless love for science, a confidence in the correctness of one's chosen path, an endurance and patience, honesty, and objectivity. Other scientists add the qualities of courage, fortitude, principleness, and skill in defending the materialist world view and the ideas of communism. Most of them consider it more critical to have the right personality (a natural ability and love for science) than to have technical knowledge, since the latter can be learned.[11]

Another dimension is the "romantic" nature of science. N. N. Semenov[12] and others maintain that beneath the "good scholar" is a romantic, one who searches for the new, who has a creative imagination, and a useful dream. Semenov claims that a passion for science derives from one's desire to unlock the mysteries of nature and to place these discoveries at the disposal of mankind for the more rapid achievement of Communist society. But, he warns, a scientist must remain objective and self-critical, so as not to be blinded by his own passionate pursuit of an "incorrect" scientific path. It is Semenov's contention that a scientist's behavior should be guided by the following characteristics: a sense of commitment to science and service to the people, a feeling of happiness for the scientific achievements of others, honesty and integrity in claiming authorship of scientific ideas, and a willingness to develop the talents and initiatives of one's students in a selfless manner.[13]

---

[11]P. T. Prikhod'ko, *Puti v nauku* (Moscow, 1973), pp. 9-10. For the relationship between a scientist's personal qualities and *partiinost'*, see P. V. Alekseev and A. Ia. Il'in, *Printsip partiinosti i estestvoznanie* (Moscow, 1972), pp. 106-113. *Partiinost'* is discussed below, pp. 78-80.

[12]N. N. Semenov, a physical chemist, received the Nobel Prize in 1956.

[13]N. N. Semenov, *Nauka i obshchestvo* (Moscow, 1973), pp. 272, 281, 293-94. Another characteristic is the social responsibility of the scientists. See below, pp. 89-91.

Although these attributes are compatible with Western notions of scientific values, they exclude specific mention of the principles used most frequently in American and British literature: *universalism* (whereby scientific laws transcend national boundaries); *communalism* (whereby substantive findings are to be communicated to, and shared with, scientists everywhere); and *organized skepticism* (whereby hypotheses are rejected or accepted on the basis of logic and empirical tests). The fourth value of science, *disinterestedness* (whereby personal prestige is not the primary goal), is referred to in Soviet criticisms of "careerism" in science. The relative lack of public attention given to universalism and communalism reflects the impact of the political and social environment on science.

It is not without significance that one of the scientists who advocates these values openly is not accepted by the official Soviet establishment. A central theme of *The Medvedev Papers*, by Zhores Medvedev, is that the norms of scientific activity require the following conditions: (1) freedom to travel and communicate with scientists from other countries, (2) an open exchange of information and criticism, and (3) freedom to cooperate and work with non-Soviet scientists.[14] Furthermore, in *The Rise and Fall of T. D. Lysenko*, Medvedev demonstrates the damage that was done in Soviet biology when organized skepticism was suppressed and disinterestedness ignored. In his case study, Medvedev has provided us with an actual historical example of the interaction between politics and the social system of science.[15]

A recent article by E. Z. Mirskaia subjects the Western conception of the scientific ethos to a detailed analysis not typical of Soviet publications.[16] Mirskaia begins with a summary of the four principles defined by Robert Merton as the ethos of science, and he mentions Bernard Barber's addition of rationalism and emotional neutrality. He shows how these principles refer simultaneously to the methodology of scientific research and to the moral behavior of scientists.

---

[14]Zhores Medvedev, *The Medvedev Papers*, trans. Vera Rich (London: Macmillan London Ltd., 1971), pp. 64, 120-27, 134, 137, 141-47.
[15]Zhores Medvedev, *The Rise and Fall of T. D. Lysenko*, trans. I. Michael Lerner (New York: Columbia University Press, 1969).
[16]E. Z. Mirskaia, "Eticheskie reguliativy funktsionirovaniia nauki," *Voprosy filosofii*, no. 3 (1975), pp. 131-38.

Mirskaia praises Merton for his delineation of these ethics and for his focus on scientific activity instead of scientific products.

Nevertheless, Mirskaia is critical of Merton in several respects. First, she complains that Merton's formulation is based on the rationalization of scientific ethics, without sufficient consideration given to the personal motives and needs of the scholar. Second, studies of the actual behavior of scientists indicate that these standards are often broken and are not, in fact, the norms of scientific activity. Mirskaia contends that Merton has presented an idealization of how scientists *should* behave rather than an observation of how they *do* behave. The result is an "ideology" of science and not an empirical description of scientific behavior. Most of all, Mirskaia feels that inadequate attention has been given to the normative changes that occur within science as society and the social relationships of science develop.[17]

There are three types of questions that prevail in Mirskaia's own analysis. Why do (some) scholars adhere to the scientific ethos? What kinds of changes among scientists lead to changes in their professional ethics? What are the essential changes in the system of values and norms that affect scientific research and discovery? Mirskaia argues that the traditional norms are not operative in all forms of contemporary scientific institutions, particularly not among applied scientists in industry. The classical ideal of scientific behavior may support the image and prestige of science, but it also creates conflict among scientists who face a discrepancy between their idealized image of science and the reality of their working conditions in scientific organizations.

Social patterns of interaction among scientists are referred to elsewhere as the immediate "environment" for scientific research. Scientists may interact within formal institutional channels or through informal networks of communication. In either case, Soviet sociologists emphasize that the scientist is working as part of a "collective." V. V. Kosolapov and A. N. Shcherban' define a "collective" as a certain type of social group that is organized on the basis of general goals and interests or according to a

---

[17]It is interesting to note that most of Mirskaia's criticisms of Merton are drawn from Western sources.

regular pattern of teamwork. A "research collective" is a group of researchers who are united by programs of scientific research and by the mutual interaction of their respective specialized duties.[18] Kosolapov and Shcherban' do not consider the freedom of science to mean an absolute liberation from the formal distribution of research responsibilities. "Such a 'freedom' is equivalent to idleness."[19] It is stressed, therefore, that scientists must participate in research collectives which have systems of management and organization, leadership, and control. This conception of a collective is very similar to Leiman's definition of a social institution, but the authors lack the broader theoretical perspective that Leiman brings to his work.

Kosolapov and Shcherban' refer primarily to the formal institutions of scientific research, but the principles of organization and leadership may be extended to the informal institutions of science as well. The "invisible college system" is a good example of an information network of communication among scientists (and other scholars). Soviet specialists in *naukovedenie* call this phenomenon the "invisible collectives" or, more frequently, "scientific schools." In *The Social-Psychological Problems of Science*, edited by M. G. Iaroshevsky, an entire section is devoted to the nature and origins of scientific schools. They are defined as "the various forms and levels of communication, interaction, and cohesion among scientists."[20] With this concept, Soviet sociology of science has moved away from traditional studies of scientific organizations and toward a more extensive and dynamic interpretation of the social system of science.

A. N. Tkachenko examines the individual and social-psychological factors necessary for the maintenance of scientific schools. He agrees with S. D. Khaitun, another contributor to the same section, that informal collectives originate in response to certain logical developments in a scientific field, that is, the emergence of certain theories

---

[18]V. V. Kosolapov and A. N. Shcherban', *Optimizatsiia nauchno-issledovatel'skoi deiatel'nosti* (Kiev, 1971), pp. 95-96.

[19]Ibid., p. 97.

[20]M. G. Iaroshevsky, ed., *Sotsial'no-psikhologicheskie problemy nauki: uchenyi i nauchnyi kollektiv* (Moscow, 1973), p. 184.

and specific scientific problems. Both authors note the importance of prominent scientists who attract a circle of colleagues and students, and who set up their own system of professional influence. Tkachenko argues, however, that the personalities of less notable scientists are just as significant in understanding the informal relationships that develop among scholars.[21]

In an innovative article, K. B. Serebrovskaia shows how scientific schools are formed and strengthened through a series of "school-conferences." The "school-conference" is a special type of communication among scholars and is distinguished from the traditional scientific conferences and symposia. Its purpose is to extend the network of informal communications among scholars and gradually to incorporate more and more people into the scientific schools, while retaining a core of scientific leadership in the center.

Using the "origin and essence of life" as an example, Serebrovskaia divides scientific fields into different levels of inquiry. Several diagrams portray these levels as a series of concentric circles with groups of researchers located in each level. Lines are drawn to indicate the "lateral ties" among scientists working within the same level and the "radial ties" among prominent scholars in different levels. Serebrovskaia then describes how scientific leaders organized three school-conferences (conferences for their scientific schools) around specific problems related to the same scientific field. As a result new channels of communication (radial and lateral ties) were developed and existing ones strengthened. The implication was that school-conferences should be held in other scientific fields to improve the exchange of information among the collectives of Soviet scientists.[22]

G. G. Diumenton's chapter in *The Sociological Problems of Science* relates the informal communication patterns among

---

[21]A. N. Tkachenko, "O kategorial'nykh predposylkakh konsolidatsii nauchnoi shkoly," and S. D. Khaitun, "O predposylkakh vozniknoveniia nauchnoi shkoly," in *Sotsial'no-psikhologicheskie problemy*, op. cit., pp. 185-89, 190-201.

[22]K. B. Serebrovskaia, "Sovremennyi neformal'nyi kollektiv v fundamental'nykh issledovaniiakh," in *Sotsial'no-psikhologicheskie problemy*, op. cit., pp. 96-127.

54

scientists to the formal organizational structures of scientific research.[23] He finds that there is an uneven concentration of personal ties in various parts of the communication network within and between laboratories and scientific establishments. In order to understand the practical implications and significance of these contacts, Diumenton advocates further research on the degrees of separation and interdependence among scientists, the mutual ties of scientists in different fields, and the criteria for the organization and distribution of scientific establishments. While concentrating on the exchange of information among scientists, Diumenton recognizes another equally important factor in contemporary scientific research, namely the social and psychological compatibility of scholars, which is discussed below.

In addition to studies of scientific collectives as a whole, Soviet scholars have focused on the scientist as an individual within the collective, since the scientist's personal needs and motives are considered important for the direction of the group's research. Kosolapov and Shcherban' agree with Kedrov and others that there is a certain internal logic of scientific development and that scientific aims are often set by society. Nevertheless, they maintain that the individual scientist is motivated by a combination of these factors with his own research interests. They view the behavioral structure of researchers in the scientific collective as a composite of three types of roles: the "conventional" formal definition of rights and duties associated with a particular position, the idiosyncratic "functional" role that a particular scientist is able to perform, and the "interpersonal" compromise between a scientist's own interests and the needs of the collective as a whole.[24] It is worth noting that, although the terminology is different, the descriptions of the first two roles pertain to the same phenomena that Western sociologists refer to as "role-expectation" and "role-performance."

With regard to the third role, several authors discuss the problem of getting the right "mix" or "balance" of

[23]G. G. Diumenton, "Issledovanie seti nauchnykh kontaktov i ego prakticheskoe znachenie," in *Sotsiologicheskie problemy*, op. cit., pp. 348-68. Diumenton's data are being analyzed in greater detail in the author's study of the invisible college system among Soviet scientists.
    [24]Kosolapov and Shcherban', pp. 98-99.

scientific fields and individual personalities in the same collective. In his article on "The Collective and Scientific Creativity," for example, Leiman comments on the gradual demise of the traditional homogeneous groups of scientists in the same discipline. He asserts that their replacement by complex teams of scientists from different specialties actually promotes the reintegration of scientific knowledge and helps to transform a group of scientists into an "organic whole."[25] It is just as probable, however, that the heterogeneous groups (in terms of training and professional fields) may have greater difficulties in resolving the potential conflicts between individual and collective interests.

Soviet scholars have demonstrated considerable concern for the conflicts that tend to develop within scientific collectives. The assumption is that scientists are easily distracted by arguments with their colleagues, which can inhibit the creative process of basic research. A few sociologists have conducted surveys to determine the sources of conflicts and ways to resolve them. One example is the study by I. V. Chernov and A. L. Shcherbakov in 1964.[26] Their sample consisted of 181 "conflicting situations" (*konfliktnye situatsii*) in various scientific institutes in Novosibirsk. Most of the people who answered the questionnaire worked in several institutes at different times, so that the problems were not limited to any specific research institute.

In their analysis of the data, Chernov and Shcherbakov conclude that there are two general causes of disputes. One is the inability of some scientists "to conduct themselves properly," which accounts for 87.1 percent of the conflicts, and includes such things as defamation of character by one's colleagues and dishonesty in the appropriation of someone else's research. The second type of problem (12.9 percent) is the failure of some institute directors, department heads, and section chiefs to "lead" (*rukovodit'*) scientists as "co-workers" (*sotrudniki*), rather than to "command" them (*komandovat'*) as "subordinates" (*podchinennye*). According

---

[25]Leiman, pp. 264, 267.
[26]I. V. Chernov and A. I. Shcherbakov, "Sotsiologicheskie voprosy organizatsii nauchnogo truda," in *Organizatsiia i effektivnost' nauchnykh issledovanii*, ed. N. A. Chinakal (Novosibirsk, 1965), pp. 139-45.

to this study, then, the reduction of tension in research institutes depends upon the ability of scientists to behave more honestly and considerately toward their colleagues and upon the finesse of those in leadership positions.[27]

Several sociologists regard the personality of administrators as an important factor for the smooth functioning of research collectives and the avoidance of conflict. For example, institute directors are expected to possess those personal qualities that enable them to organize research teams and supervise their work, to maintain an effective control over the use of scientific resources, and to establish a congenial environment for cooperative research. Kosolapov and Shcherban' contend that there are additional sources of conflict related to the nature of scientific organization and development. For example, the scholar may resent the limitations imposed on his research by administrative plans, or the scientist may have to change his professional orientation to meet the demands of a rapidly changing field.[28]

At one level of analysis, Soviet sociologists have studied the relationships between the system of scientific research and the larger social environment; at another level, they have examined the compatibility between individual scientists and the collective. In both cases, science is viewed as a form of social activity, whether organized into the traditional structures of laboratories and institutes or according to the more flexible "scientific schools." As a system of social behavior, the research activities of the scientist are vulnerable to influences from the social environment. The perception of new ideas in science becomes a combined product of the social conditions and the personal characteristics of the scientist. Therefore, the next section considers the ways in which Soviet scholars have analyzed the impact of both social and psychological factors on scientific work.

---

[27]Ibid., pp. 140-42, 144.
[28]Kosolapov and Shcherban', pp. 132-34.

III. Social-Psychological Aspects of Scientific Research

Soviet treatment of the social conditions of science and the social-psychology of scientific discovery are rooted firmly in Marxism-Leninism. The socialist system is portrayed as a more advanced form of socioeconomic structure than capitalism. By definition, socialism is supposed to provide conditions that promote the advancement of science and encourage progress in other spheres of human activity. Indeed, the goals of communism and the goals of science are often presented as one and the same, that is, the ability of mankind to control the forces of nature, thereby obtaining freedom and self-fulfillment. Within this context, several authors stress the importance of socialism for scientific and technical progress in general, while others focus directly on the advantages it has for scientific discovery.

One of the scholars who compares the effects of socialism and capitalism on science is E. A. Arab-Ogly. He treats the "historical incompatibility of the scientific-technical revolution and capitalism" in terms of the deep contradiction between the capitalist means of production and science as a sphere of socially useful activity. He maintains that science produces socially useful knowledge, whereas capitalism produces items earmarked for individual consumption. The values of science and capitalism are inconsistent, because the entrepreneur evaluates new ideas in terms of their immediate monetary value rather than their long-term social impact. In other words, the interests of private capital are said to be in basic conflict with the interests of science and society.[1] The irony of this argument is that many Soviet scholars have tried to use "economic effectiveness" as a basis for evaluating Soviet scientific research. Their

[1]E. A. Arab-Ogly, "O sotsial'nykh posledstviiakh nauchno-tekhnicheskoi revoliutsii," in *Nauchno-tekhnicheskaia revoliutsiia i obshchestvennyi progress* (Moscow, 1969), pp. 21-30.

presumption, of course, is that the economic benefits derived from Soviet science will be more "in the interests of society" (however defined) than in the interests of only one class.

Kosolapov and Shcherban' also refer to the general impact that social structures have on scientific activities in the Soviet Union and the United States. They describe how the social organizations that administer scientific research under socialism are accessible to scientists, so that a system of "self-regulation" actually develops. In fact, leading Soviet scientists are members of the academic councils within scientific research organizations, and many are party members. The councils exercise considerable influence in the selection of research themes and in the general activities of academy institutes.[2] By contrast, according to Kosolapov and Shcherban', scientific research in capitalist countries is organized and administered by a separate group of people (for example, a board of trustees), so that scientists do not have as much of an impact on the regulation of scientific work.[3]

Indeed, at the present time, it appears that the Soviet scientific elite may have more direct access than American scientists to government decisions regarding science policy. This view is based on the current diffusion of scientific power at the top levels of the United States government. Nevertheless, lower-ranking scientists in the United States have greater opportunities to use public channels of influence than their counterparts in the Soviet Union. With regard to the administration of science in research institutes, however, there seems to be a greater tendency in the USSR for scientists to become "science-administrators." Such a practice would support the above argument that Soviet scientists are more directly in control of their own research.[4]

---

[2]For an analysis of the role of Soviet scientists in policymaking, see Linda Lubrano Greenberg, "Policymaking in the USSR Academy of Sciences," *Journal of Contemporary History*, no. 4 (1973), pp. 67-80.

[3]V. V. Kosolapov and A. N. Shcherban', *Optimizatsiia nauchno-issledovatel'skoi deiatel'nosti* (Kiev, 1971), p. 100.

[4]The relationships between research and administrative roles are being examined by Linda L. Lubrano in "A Comparative Analysis of the Career Patterns of Soviet and American Scientists," study in progress.

The close relationship between the social environment and creativity is the particular focus of Kosolapov's and Shcherban's analysis. They describe the scientist's social surroundings as the "macroclimate of the scientific milieu." This represents the aggregate of social conditions that influence the activities of scientific collectives, define the direction of scientific research, and formulate the inner convictions of the scholar. The nature of the impact of the social environment on the scientist's work is considered to be dependent upon the following factors: (1) the degree of correspondence between the scholar's ideological world view and that prevailing in society; (2) the role of scholars as a social group and their influence in defining the goals of society; (3) the degree of correspondence between social goals and the internal logic of scientific development; (4) the tempo of the assimilation of scientific achievements; (5) the level of development of intranational and international communication among scientists; and (6) the level of education for those people who are not in scientific collectives.[5]

The two authors elaborate upon the issue of the correspondence between the scholar's individual view and those prevailing in society. Science is seen as only one form of social consciousness. It exists alongside the ideas of politics, morality, art, and philosophy. It is natural for the scientist to believe in the values and concepts that prevail in his society, since he is surrounded by a totality of social conditions which he cannot completely ignore. In addition, he is influenced by traditional professional ethics which he "automatically" follows and which affect his moral behavior and research.[6] The scholar's consciousness is viewed, therefore, as a complex combination of social and scientific experiences, which ultimately affect his ability to be creative and successful in science.

In order not to leave the impression that the scientist is completely controlled by the macroclimate of prevailing ideas, Kosolapov and Shcherban' insist that the very nature of scientific research demands an individual and original approach to unresolved scientific problems. They say that "monism," or scientific agreement, should characterize only the settled areas of science, whereas a "pluralism" of ideas

---

[5]Kosolapov and Shcherban', p. 108.
[6]Ibid., pp. 110-11.

should flourish in issues that are unresolved. Creativity at this level of science is considered completely compatible with the acceptance of a socialist world view. The arguments for individuality in science and the influence of social values converge when the authors conclude that, since socialism by its very nature provides a scientific world view, the scientist in a socialist country can be most innovative in his research when accepting the prevailing ideology of society.[7]

The personal characteristics of scientists in relation to their social environment are given greater attention by M. G. Iaroshevsky, head of the Sector on Scientific Creativity in the Institute for the History of Natural Science and Technology. Iaroshevsky has written extensively about the impact of a scientist's perception, motivation, and personality on scientific discovery. In one of his publications he tries to relate the logical structure of science (its concepts and categories) to the perception of new ideas. He makes a distinction between the scientist's focus on "reality" and his background in conceptual schemes. It is asserted that the discovery of facts and regularities tend to depend more upon a scientist's direct observation of reality than upon his cognitive tools and methods (although the two are closely intertwined). Iaroshevsky agrees with those who believe that the prevailing scientific categories (or paradigms) form a potential barrier to scientific perception, and he therefore advocates greater research and probing into the logical inner structure of scientific theories.[8] In "The Perception of Discovery as a Problem of *Naukovedenie*," he joins Mikulinsky in arguing that discoveries often occur from unsuccessful attempts to resolve a scientific problem and from sudden "flashes of genius."[9]

In his article on "The External and Inner Motivation of Scientific Creativity," Iaroshevsky makes a distinction between the cognitive and motivational aspects of scientific

---

[7]Ibid., p. 109.
[8]M. G. Iaroshevsky, "Kategorial'nyi stroi nauki i psikhologiia vospriiatiia otkrytiia," in *Nauchnoe otkrytie i ego vospriiatie*, ed. S. R. Mikulinsky and M. G. Iaroshevsky (Moscow, 1971), pp. 125-34.
[9]S. R. Mikulinsky and M. G. Iaroshevsky, "Vospriiatie otkrytiia kak naukovedcheskaia problema," in *Nauchnoe otkrytie*, op. cit., p. 12.

creativity. Since the scientist's principal purpose is to produce new knowledge, more attention has been given to the cognitive processes of discovery. Yet, Iaroshevsky asserts, the scientist's motivation may be a more significant key to the understanding of scientific creativity. He is critical, however, of the sources of data used in most motivational research, that is, surveys of scientists' opinions and attitudes concerning their own motives.

> Motives have their own objective dynamics. They take shape in the real system of relations between the individual and society, between the individual and the world. This system is incomparably more complex than that which is reflected in any subject's self-report.[10]

He insists that "the authors of self-reports do not have the special conceptual and methodological tools required for an investigation of this reality," and elsewhere he likens this approach to a sick person being his own doctor.[11]

Iaroshevsky differentiates between the concepts of "external" and "inner" motives and defines them in terms of their relationship to the developing system of science and not in relation to the individual scientist. He says that science develops according to its own laws, laws that operate independently of the personal attributes of the scholar. "Inner" motivation is part of the continual unfolding of scientific knowledge, which takes place during the interaction between the logic of science and the readiness of the scientist to perceive it. It is an "inner" motive that moves a scientist to immerse himself in the search for effective solutions to the current problems of science; however, a scientist's personal ambitions and drive are considered "external" motives because they are outside the logical development of scientific thought. Iaroshevsky feels that

---

[10]Mikhail Yaroshevsky (*sic*), "The External and Inner Motivation of Scientific Creativity," *Social Sciences*, no. 1 (1974), p. 61.

[11]Ibid., p. 60; S. R. Mikulinsky and M. G. Yaroshevsky (*sic*), "Apperception of a Scientific Discovery as a Problem of the Science of Science," trans. Maria Hoser, *Zagadnienia naukoznawstwa* (1970), pp. 69-70.

these two types of motivation are potentially in conflict and should be given greater study.[12]

The terms "inner" and "external" motives may seem confusing at first, because they have different connotations in Western literature (where motives are defined in relation to the individual). Nevertheless, Iaroshevsky's distinction is very useful for clarifying the Soviet conception of the development of scientific knowledge. According to this view, the laws of nature have their own "inner" dynamics and exist independently of human perception. People are part of nature, but their personal drives and ambitions are considered "external," although not irrelevant, to the logical development of scientific ideas. A scientific phenomenon cannot be discovered prior to that time in history when the necessary knowledge for the discovery has been accumulated. Nevertheless, individuals and social institutions play critical "external" roles in the perception and acceptance of the "inner" dynamics of the laws of nature.

Mikulinsky and Iaroshevsky believe that at certain stages in the historical development of science the "soil is ready" for particular discoveries. In another joint article they call the combined process of the perception and appraisal of new ideas the "apperception" of a scientific discovery. The word "perception" in science is used in a broader sense than that adopted in modern psychology. It includes the grasping of scientific ideas and their conceptual interpretation and assessment, which means that the scientist usually expresses new concepts in terms of the logical structure of science. However, the authors emphasize the "blindness to a new idea or its warped perception" that can result from the paradigms prevailing in the scientific community.[13] Mikulinsky and Iaroshevsky maintain that a major obstacle to scientific discovery is the natural resistance to something new (sometimes a "pathological" reaction to change), which is not at all compatible with the image of a scientist as a person with an "open mind." In

---

[12]Yaroshevsky (*sic*), "External and Inner Motivation," pp. 67-68.
[13]Mikulinsky and Yaroshevsky (*sic*), "Apperception," pp. 68, 75. Although he is not referred to in their article, this point is developed further by Thomas Kuhn, *The Structure of Scientific Revolutions* (Chicago: University of Chicago Press, 1962).

support of their view, they cite Bernard Barber's comment that all scientists are either experiencing resistance to established theories or are themselves resisting new ideas.[14]

The perception of a new idea is conditioned further by the peculiarities of the scientific and social environment in a given historical period. Once the discovery is made it needs to be accepted by the scientific community before it can be incorporated into the existing body of knowledge. Mikulinsky and Iaroshevsky refer to this as the evaluation (or appraisal) stage of scientific discovery, whereby the importance of the idea is assessed by other scientists. As a rule, the significance of a scientific discovery is determined by the nature of the shift it makes in the established conceptual schemes of science.[15]

Mikulinsky and Iaroshevsky would prefer that this judgment be made by specialists in *naukovedenie*. They feel that the scientist's desire to add his own ideas to the existing body of knowledge leads to an exaggeration of his personal claim to truth and a resistance to the ideas of others, particularly if "a scientist has no other possibility of affirming his own ego than by producing new information."[16] In conclusion, then, Mikulinsky and Iaroshevsky contend that an individual's creativity is very much affected by the evaluative mechanisms that control the generation and acceptance of ideas. The degree to which this influences his work depends upon the scientist's own perception of the evaluative process and on the self-serving nature of his discovery.

I. I. Leiman, the late N. I. Rodny, A. A. Malinovsky, and B. A. Frolov add their thoughts on creativity in a collection of essays edited by Mikulinsky and Iaroshevsky.[17] Leiman regards creativity as the highest form of human labor, resulting from the skills, intuition, and devotion of individual scientists. He shows concern over the distribution system of scientific information, the complexity of scientific research, and the problems of science management, all of which are potential obstacles to the full development of

---

[14]Mikulinsky and Iaroshevsky, "Vospriiatie otkrytiia," pp. 7-9.
[15]Mikulinsky and Yaroshevsky (*sic*), "Apperception," p. 68.
[16]Ibid., p. 74.
[17]S. R. Mikulinsky and M. G. Iaroshevsky, eds. *Nauchnoe tvorchestvo* (Moscow, 1969).

each scientist's creative potential.[18] While Leiman emphasizes the social factors impinging upon scientific discovery,
Rodny and Malinovsky bring in some of the logical and personal aspects of creativity.

Rodny treats the concept of discovery in great detail
and distinguishes among four types: the creation of new conceptual schemes, the finding of scientific laws, the revela-
tions of new phenomena, and the inventions of basically new
instruments.[19] Discoveries contribute something new to science and give rise to a series of investigations, so that
there is a chain reaction of new concepts, theories, and
methods of research. Rodny dwells particularly on the relationship between the first two types of discovery and the
third. He rejects the notion that the discovery process is
always inductive, that is, that new theories are responses
to facts that do not "fit" the prevailing paradigm. It is
his contention that the relationship is often reversed, since
theories themselves generate the search for supportive facts.
In this way, the development and testing of theories contributes to the revelation of new phenomena.[20]

The implication is that scientific theories might also
give rise to inventions, since they stimulate the search for
how certain relationships would "work" in practice. An in-
vention represents the physical creation of something that
did not exist previously. Therefore, other analysts sometimes distinguish it from a discovery, which reveals something that existed prior to our knowledge of it. Rodny dis-
agrees with this view and suggests, instead, that there is
an element of discovery in the very process of creating inventions, that is, the revelation of relationships among
phenomena for the first time.[21] In turn, mechanical inventions could lead to the further discovery of scientific laws
and the creation of new theories.

---

[18]I. I. Leiman, "Kollektiv i nauchnoe tvorchestvo," in
Nauchnoe tvorchestvo, op. cit., pp. 261-70.
    [19]N. I. Rodny, "Nekotorye aspekty problemy nauchnykh
otkrytii," in *Nauchnoe tvorchestvo*, op. cit., p. 146.
    [20]Ibid., pp. 147-49. He does not deny, however, that ex-
perimentation and new information, in turn, stimulate the
synthesis of ideas and the creation of new concepts and
theories.
    [21]Ibid., pp. 145-46.

Regardless of whether scientific discoveries are the
result of "theoretical determinism" or "accidental" observation, Rodny believes that the probability of their occur-
rence is enhanced by social interest in the research area and
the technical means whereby the new phenomenon can be ob-
served.[22] Elsewhere he considers the personal characteristics
of scientists, such as age, intuition, imagination, and the
breadth or depth of one's knowledge, as additional elements
in the creative process.[23] In the 1972 symposium on scientific biographies, Rodny directly confronts the issue of
whether the logic of science or the psychological attributes
of the scientist are more significant for scientific discovery. He notes the fact that certain scholars respond more
adequately than others to the "call of the times"; nevertheless, he concludes that the "logical situation" prevailing
in science is the *key* to an understanding of why and how
certain discoveries occur.[24]

Malinovsky's contribution to the volume on *Scientific
Creativity* focuses upon the mental conditions of the creative process. He defines creativity as the "re-working of
the information we receive, with the aim of extracting its
maximum content."[25] Human thought is analyzed as the selection of associations and patterns from available information;
however, the creative process is more complex than this.
According to Malinovsky, it includes the development of su-
perfluous ideas, which are partly or wholly rejected, and
which stimulate the emergence of new combinations of ideas
and hypotheses. An essential ingredient is the "excitement"
(*vozbudimost'*) felt by the scientist as he sees new patterns
in existing formation. Some people have the capacity to
conceptualize very unusual, sometimes absurd, ideas which
serve as a source of inspiration to other scientists.
Malinovsky contrasts this type of person with one who

[22]Ibid., pp. 153, 155.
[23]N. I. Rodny, "Problemy nauchnogo tvorchestva i
organizatsii nauki v trudakh estestvoispytatelei," in *Ocherki
istorii i teorii razvitiia nauki*, ed. V. S. Bibler, B. S.
Griaznov, and S. R. Mikulinsky (Moscow, 1969), pp. 151-68,
176-85.
[24]N. I. Rodny, "Biografiia i logika," in *Chelovek nauki*,
ed. M. G. Iaroshevsky (Moscow, 1974), pp. 144-51.
[25]A. A. Malinovsky, "K voprosu o putiakh issledovaniia
uslovii tvorcheskogo protsessa," in *Nauchnoe tvorchestvo*,
op. cit., p. 282.

skillfully develops the ideas of others, and he maintains that both qualities are important for the advancement of science.[26]

The mental process by which the scientist sorts out his data is very critical and is vulnerable to pressures from the scientific community. Malinovsky warns that excessive dependence on the social environment can have an inhibiting effect on the initial stages of scientific discovery, and he therefore proposes that scientists be allowed to explore their new ideas fully before being subjected to criticisms from colleagues with opposing points of view.[27] In reality, however, it is difficult for the scientist to ignore the opinions of other scientists in his collective, and continual interaction may actually contribute to the more rapid development of new ideas.

In the same book B. A. Frolov examines the initial motivations that lead a person to join a scientific collective and to collaborate in the experimentation with new ideas. He lists inquisitiveness, personal aggrandizement, and social inducements as three key motives for an individual's pursuit of scientific discoveries in the United States; and he notes a conflict between creativity and the drive for personal success. Frolov asserts that the same motivations exist among Soviet scientists, but the "spirit of the scientific collective" (in the USSR) transforms individual ambitions into socially useful creativity. In contrast to Malinovsky, therefore, he regards the collective as an essential form of scientific interaction and an impetus to scientific discoveries.[28]

In *Naukovedenie*, P. A. Rachkov agrees with Frolov that the collective is important, but he also supports Malinovsky's view that it may threaten the sense of individuality that is a basic part of scientific discovery. Among the personal factors that Rachkov regards as essential to scientific creativity are the scientist's intuition, imagination, passion, "flights of thought," and other characteristics outside

---

[26] Ibid., pp. 283-86.
[27] Ibid., pp. 287-88.
[28] B. A. Frolov, "Kollektiv i motivatsiia tvorchestva," in *Nauchnoe tvorchestvo*, op. cit., pp. 271-80.

the formal logic of science.[29] He mentions some of the same
material motives noted by Frolov, such as personal gain, the
competitive spirit, and "happiness in the attainment of
truth."[30] Regarding the last motive, Rachkov believes that
scientists feel an aesthetic satisfaction in the acquisition
of knowledge and its application to social needs.[31] In order
for scientific collectives to be more innovative, therefore,
their leaders must recognize and stimulate the variety of
emotions, talents, and habits of individual scientists.
Otherwise, as suggested by Mikulinsky and others, the social
environment might crush the creative spirit of science.

---

[29]P. A. Rachkov, *Naukovedenie: problemy, struktura,
elementy* (Moscow, 1974), pp. 142, 146.

[30]Ibid., p. 149.

[31]Ibid., pp. 151-52.

IV. The Organization and Management of Scientific Research

The social factors that influence scientific creativity are not necessarily the same as those that affect scientific productivity. Creativity is part of scientific discovery and innovation; productivity is often regarded as the application of knowledge to the national economy.[1] While a scientist's motives and perceptions comprise an important area of analysis, Soviet sociologists of science are just as concerned with the way scientific work is formally organized and managed. The assumption is that greater efficiency in the organization of science will raise its productivity. It can be argued that Soviet studies of the social-psychological conditions for scientific research are themselves directed toward the social management of science. Indeed, there is a close relationship between information regarding the scientist's behavior within his collective and the planning and control of that behavior.

One of the first prerequisites for science management is to take inventory of the level and distribution of scientific manpower and to relate that to the overall patterns of scientific development. Two of the sociologists who include some statistical data as part of their overall assessment of Soviet science are G. N. Volkov and I. I. Leiman. Volkov evaluates Soviet scientific potential in terms of the number of scientists and engineers, the amount of equipment in research institutes, the production of scientific instruments, the centers of scientific documentation, and the quantity of scientific publications. He discusses problems concerning the distribution of scientists among specialized fields and the distribution of funds among the different stages of

---

[1]This is not its only meaning, however. Soviet scholars refer to the productivity of science also in terms of the observable output of scientific research, such as publications and patents.

scientific research and development.[2] Leiman looks at the growth of science in terms of four indicators: the number of publications, the number of scientific workers, the amount of financing, and the number of basic discoveries. He presents graphs and tables of data for each indicator along with his own interpretations.[3] Both scholars make occasional comparisons with the United States, but unfortunately their information is out of date, and little attention is devoted to estimates of future trends.[4]

Forecasting future needs and the growth of scientific resources is an important part of a recent publication by V. N. Klimeniuk. In the *Control of the Development and Utilization of Scientific Potential*,[5] Klimeniuk takes inventory of the educational backgrounds of Soviet scientists and provides data on scientific personnel in different regions, especially the Ukraine. He compares the number of specialists in the USSR with those in the United States as well as the scientific expenditures of both countries. Since the book is directed toward an improvement in planning, it also includes sections on problems related to the material-technical provisions for science, the organization of labor, and the effective utilization of scientific manpower.

---

[2]G. N. Volkov, *Sotsiologiia nauki. Sotsiologicheskie ocherki nauchno-tekhnicheskoi deiatel'nosti* (Moscow, 1968), pp. 217-37.

[3]I. I. Leiman, *Nauka kak sotsial'nyi institut* (Leningrad, 1971), pp. 69-94.

[4]Future trends in Soviet and American scientific manpower are being studied by other Soviet scholars. See, for example, F. V. Rossel's, "Metody prognozirovaniia chislennosti i struktury nauchnykh kadrov," in *Nauchno-tekhnicheskaia revoliutsiia i izmenenie struktury nauchnykh kadrov SSSR*, ed. D. M. Gvishiani, S. R. Mikulinsky, and S. A. Kugel' (Moscow, 1973), pp. 176-99; and F. V. Rossel's, "Prognozirovanie nauchno-tekhnicheskikh kadrov v SShA," in *Problemy deiatel'nosti uchenogo i nauchnykh kollektivov*, vol. V, ed. S. A. Kugel' (Leningrad, 1973), pp. 216-20.

[5]V. N. Klimeniuk, *Upravlenie razvitiem i ispol'zovaniem nauchnogo potentsiala* (Kiev, 1974). Another useful source on the preparation and distribution of specialists is K. P. Savichev, *Podgotovka i raspredelenie molodykh spetsialistov v SSSR* (Moscow, 1972).

Some of the best work on the quality and distribution of Soviet scientists has been done by S. A. Kugel' and his colleagues. Two of their books on this subject are *The Scientific-Technical Revolution and the Change in the Structure of Scientific Cadres in the USSR*, edited by D. M. Gvishiani, S. R. Mikulinsky, and S. A. Kugel',[6] and *Scientific Cadres of Leningrad*, edited by S. A. Kugel', B. D. Lebin, and the late Iu. S. Meleshchenko.[7] Kugel' is the main author of the first publication, which includes contributions from E. M. Sidorova, N. K. Serov, and F. V. Rossel's. The book is divided into two parts: one considers the methodological problems of studying the structure and dynamics of scientific manpower; and the other is an analysis of changes in scientific personnel in the USSR between 1950 and 1970. A lengthy appendix provides sources of data, an attempt at mathematical modeling, and examples of forecasting techniques.

Kugel' defines the "dynamics of scientific cadres" in terms of their numerical growth and professional mobility. The latter includes their redistribution among different types of institutes and the changes in their systems of training. There are several statistical tables concerning the total number of Soviet scientific workers between 1950 and 1970. For the same period, Kugel' gives a breakdown of the number of scientists in each scientific field and relates this to their degree qualifications. He includes tables on the demographic variables of age and sex and comments on their relationships to scientific creativity. Subsequent data on "job structure" show the distribution of scientists among different occupational positions and types of organizations.

There is an underlying logic and consistency to the entire book, with the possible exception of a chapter by Sidorova on industrial institutes. The concepts of "scientific worker" and "scientific institute" are defined clearly in the appendix, which also describes the classification system of the USSR Central Statistical Administration. Soviet government statistics constitute the main source of information, although some references are made to the use of

---

[6]D. M. Gvishiani, S. R. Mikulinsky, and S. A. Kugel', eds., *Nauchno-tekhnicheskaia revoliutsiia*, op. cit.
[7]S. A. Kugel', B. D. Lebin, and Iu. S. Meleshchenko, eds., *Nauchnye kadry Leningrada* (Leningrad, 1973).

survey data. The data categories and format of presentation
are coherent and systematic. It is unfortunate, however,
that Kugel' has not subjected his vast amount of information
to more sophisticated statistical analysis.

Scientific Cadres of Leningrad differs from the first
book in two important respects. One, of course, is the
focus on a single city. The authors express an obvious
pride toward Leningrad as "one of the most important industrial, scientific, and cultural centers of the country."[8]
This is borne out by some of the statistics. For example,
scientific workers in the Academy institutes of Leningrad
have higher degree qualifications than scientists in the
USSR Academy of Sciences as a whole.[9] The data are useful
for comparisons with the status of scientists elsewhere in
the Soviet Union.

A second difference between the two publications is the
utilization of survey data in the Leningrad volume. A
questionnaire was distributed to 2,000 scientific workers in
academic, machine-building, and industrial establishments of
Leningrad between 1968 and 1971. The analysis of the data
focuses on three general areas: (1) the mobility of scientists among different professional fields, the reasons they
give for changing fields, and the impact of requalification
on their work; (2) the relationship of the individual to his
scientific collective and his participation in collective
publications; and (3) the motives and satisfaction of
scientific workers with regard to their mobility among professional fields.

In each of these areas of inquiry, the data are meaningful but limited. It is obvious that much of the data has
not been published. Different portions of the original
sample are included in each table, so that it is difficult
to make cross-tabular comparisons, and generally the techniques of data processing employed throughout the book are
rudimentary and incomplete. The authors should have provided
more information on the procedures of sample selection, and
the questionnaire itself should have been included in an
appendix. The rest of the volume follows the same format
and data categories (that is, professional fields, qualifications, sex, and age) that appear in the other book edited

---

[8]Ibid., p. 23.
[9]Ibid., p. 48.

by Kugel', except for greater detail in the listing of occupational positions. Also, there are brief sections on social-class background, the evaluation and payment of scientific workers, and the "ideological-political education of scientific cadres" (which seems peculiarly out of place). Despite some of the above-mentioned limitations, both books provide useful sources of data on Soviet scientific manpower.

The distribution of Soviet scientific personnel is only one aspect of the organization of science and should be considered in conjunction with other elements of science management. The concept of "scientific organization" is developed by Iu. M. Sheinin in *The Organization of Scientific Activities*, which he coedited with E. A. Beliaev and S. R. Mikulinsky. As a result of the vast changes from the scientific-technical revolution, science has become both the "subject" and "object" of organization.[10] By this Sheinin means that scientific principles have penetrated organization theory, while science itself has become a more complex and highly organized activity. When science is studied as a static system, it includes the formal structures and institutions of scientific research. As a dynamic process, however, it refers to the activities that transform the existing structures through goal-oriented management and government planning.

Sheinin looks at scientific organization in both its "narrow" and "broader" contexts. In its more limited sense, he argues, the current institutions of science are inadequate for the rapidly changing nature of scientific development. He repeats a view voiced frequently by Mikulinsky and other Soviet scholars, namely that institutes organized on a disciplinary basis should be restructured for research on particular problems. In a broader context, Sheinin feels that science should be applied to the organization of society. Science is becoming a "leading branch of social production," and society is becoming more dependent on the scientific-technical intelligentsia.[11]

Sheinin suggests that, in the future, government organization of science will not be necessary, since science will

---

[10]Iu. M. Sheinin, "Nauka i organizatsiia," in *Organizatsiia nauchnoi deiatel'nosti*, ed. E. A. Beliaev et al. (Moscow, 1968), pp. 108-9.
[11]Ibid., pp. 109-22.

be able to regulate itself.[12]   Nevertheless, most of the
contributors to *The Organization of Scientific Activities*
discuss the need for improvements in the institutional
structure of scientific research, rather than the establishment of self-regulating mechanisms.   Mikulinsky, for example, voices some skepticism toward the scientists' ability
to appraise the overall needs of scientific development, and
he wonders whether their involvement in science planning has
been too narrow-minded and self-centered.   As he and other
observers have noted with regard to the vested interests of
some scientists, "It is easier to create tens of new laboratories and departments than to close one old, exhausted unit.
This leads to unproductive expenditures and lowers the efficiency of scientific research."[13]

The effectiveness of scientific organizations is analyzed in *The Organization of Science* by G. M. Dobrov, V. M.
Klimeniuk, V. M. Odrin, and A. A. Savel'ev[14] and *Labor in
the Sphere of Science* by P. N. Zavlin, A. I. Shcherbakov,
and M. A. Iudelevich.[15]   Dobrov and his colleagues review
the general characteristics of modern science, such as the
increased size of research institutes.   Changes in the scope
of "big science" have affected the scientist's working conditions and have created new problems for science planning
and management.   The coauthors use survey data to uncover
some of the difficulties within scientific organizations;
and they find that the effectiveness of scientific work
depends upon the hierarchy of working relationships, the
"morale" of the collective, the information system, and the
allocation of time among different activities.   They conclude,
however, that the "optimum structure" of scientific work
still depends on variables mentioned frequently in the literature, that is, the distribution of degrees, the balance
of professional fields, and the average age of scientists
within research collectives.

Zavlin, Shcherbakov, and Iudelevich also use question-
naires to acquire information on a scientist's personal

[12] Ibid., p. 124.
[13] S. R. Mikulinsky, "Nekotorye problemy organizatsii
nauchnoi deiatel'nosti i ee izucheniia," in *Organizatsiia,*
op. cit., pp. 139-40, 142.
[14] G. M. Dobrov et al., *Organizatsiia nauki* (Kiev, 1970).
[15] P. N. Zavlin, A. I. Shcherbakov, and M. A. Iudelevich,
Trud v sfere nauki, 2d ed. (Moscow, 1973).

characteristics (age, education, and so forth), daily allocation of time, motives, and work satisfaction. They place more emphasis, however, on the research-production cycle, which forms the basis for their classification of different types of scientific labor.[16] Zavlin and his colleagues assume that the creation of a "scientific organization of labor" (that is, the use of social science data to improve the management of science) would shorten the time span between research and production and would raise the social productivity of science. The goal is to hasten the economic and social application of scientific knowledge. Therefore, the coauthors deal with the elusive problem of evaluating the cost of a scientific product, and they try to develop formulas that combine the economic and social value of scientific research.

While Dobrov, Zavlin, and their colleagues search for factors that will *improve* the organization of science, other scholars simply *describe* the institutional dynamics of scientific research. Still others relate both forms of information to the management and control of science. Probably the most useful single source for a recent description of Soviet scientific institutions is *The Basic Principles and General Problems of Science Management*, edited by D. M. Gvishiani and A. A. Zvorykin.[17] It has several charts that depict the organizational structure of science in the USSR as a whole, and there are descriptions of research in academic, industrial, and educational establishments. It is significant that the authors look at science as a network of organizations that are an organic part of the larger system of social and political controls.

In chapter three, "The Basic Principles of Science Policy in the USSR," Gvishiani says that the government bears primary responsibility for the management and control of science. Governments have to coordinate the mobilization of resources for the rapid development of scientific research, and for this reason, Gvishiani notes, many governments have established specialized organs for the formulation and execution of science policy. Science policies represent the set of measures taken by legislative and administrative

---

[16]Ibid., pp. 32-39.
[17]D. M. Gvishiani and A. A. Zvorykin, eds., *Osnovnye printsipy i obshchie problemy upravleniia naukoi* (Moscow, 1973).

organs in the fields of science and technology.[18] He argues
that it is necessary to strengthen the Soviet government's
role in this area by centralizing the administration of
science in the USSR.

Gvishiani's views are presented in greater detail in
the first volume of *Management, Planning and the Organization of Scientific and Technical Researches*, where he gives
six reasons for a centralized system of science management:
(1) the complexities of science, (2) the massive flow of
scientific information, and (3) the problems of obtaining
expensive equipment and instruments. Further, a centralized
science leadership can guarantee (4) the use of rational
planning in research, (5) the protection of scientists'
patent rights, and (6) an effective means of cooperating
with scientists in other countries.[19] The centralized
organization and management of science would be buttressed
by social research and statistical data that allow the
leaders to forecast and plan the development of science and
technology.[20]

It is worth noting, at this point, that Mikulinsky
refers frequently to the important role played by specialists on *naukovedenie* in providing the necessary data for
planning the organization of science. He and others have
argued that it is difficult to predict the short-term
results of greater efficiency in scientific research. Even
on a long-term basis, one cannot always know the potential
significance of different directions of fundamental (or
exploratory) research. Mikulinsky contends that the social
scientist who is studying the overall regularities of
scientific development is best qualified to deal with these
problems and to identify those branches of science that
promise new discoveries or great practical achievements.[21]

---

[18]D. M. Gvishiani, "Osnovnye printsipy nauchnoi
politiki SSSR," in *Osnovnye printsipy*, op. cit., p. 38.
    [19]D. M. Gvishiani, "Sotsial'naia rol' nauki i politika
gosudarstva v oblasti nauki," in *Nauka: upravlenie,
planirovanie, organizatsiia*, ed. G. Kh. Popov, vol. I of
*Upravlenie, planirovanie i organizatsiia nauchnykh i
tekhnicheskikh issledovanii*, ed. D. M. Gvishiani (Moscow,
1970), pp. 52-53.
    [20]Ibid., pp. 43-47.
    [21]For example, see Mikulinsky, "Nekotorye problemy,"
pp. 137-49.

76

Regardless of the source of information and the specific form of science organization (centralized or decentralized), the purpose of science management remains the same, that is, the efficient administration and regulation of scientific activities. Compared with Gvishiani, two of the sociologists mentioned earlier take a more general and theoretical approach to the subject, but the implications of social control are similar. Leiman, for example, defines "management" (upravlenie) as a general social phenomenon, arising wherever the collective action of people is directed toward a common goal. The efficiency of any collective (including a social institution) is dependent upon the nature of its management. The administration of science is seen as a combination of political, scientific, and organizational factors, whereby government planning is combined with scientific expertise and management skills.[22]

From another perspective, Maizel' relates science to a cybernetic system of self-regulation. "The processes of management appear necessarily as information processes."[23] The implication is that science provides knowledge of human behavior in the form of information, which is then used to regulate that behavior--including the behavior of the scientists themselves. Therefore, the term "science management" can refer both to the management of science and to management by science. Studies of science organizations and their patterns of internal and external interactions provide academic inputs to decisions regarding science management, but the processes through which these decisions are made and enforced are inherently political.

Two sources that focus directly on the politics of science are Naukovedenie by P. A. Rachkov[24] and The Principle of Partiinost' and Natural Science by P. V. Alekseev and A. Ia. Il'in.[25] Rachkov contends that science is often used by governments to strengthen the political influence of their countries. "Science is becoming . . . an important political factor having a wide [and] direct significance in

---

[22]Leiman, pp. 133-34.
[23]I. A. Maizel', Nauka, avtomatizatsiia, obshchestvo (Leningrad, 1972), p. 101.
[24]P. A. Rachkov, Naukovedenie: problemy, struktura, elementy (Moscow, 1974), chap. 5.
[25]P. V. Alekseev and A. Ia. Il'in, Printsip partiinosti i estestvoznanie (Moscow, 1972).

the realization not only of domestic, but also of international policies."[26] For this reason, Rachkov feels that it is incumbent upon the Soviet government to establish a unified national science policy. He proposes that such a policy should include (1) decisions regarding the main directions of scientific research, (2) the maintenance of continual growth in scientific institutions and manpower, and (3) an efficient application of scientific products.[27]

In his discussion of science policy, Rachkov also considers the leading role played by the Communist party in the "political management" of scientific research and development. The party analyzes the interaction between scientific and social needs; it defines science's strategic goals, as well as its (anticipated) social and political consequences. Rachkov asserts that the responsibilities of the party include an identification of the most important paths of impending scientific discoveries, a maintenance of adequate expenditures for the application of scientific achievements, a raising of the efficiency of science planning, and an improvement of the "moral atmosphere" within scientific collectives. Together the Communist party and Soviet government are expected to "create and perfect a new type of social organization of science."[28]

In *The Principle of Partiinost' and Natural Science* Alekseev and Il'in demonstrate the relationship between the party and science through the principle of *partiinost'*. Most of their book is devoted to a philosophical treatment of this concept within the framework of dialectical materialism and social-historical change. The authors explain that *partiinost'* has a different meaning for various sectors of society. With regard to science, *partiinost'* supposedly provides the "spiritual" orientation necessary to deal with the social consequences of scientific and technical change.

The interaction between *partiinost'* and science can be described as follows: Science deals with the "objective" aspects of human knowledge, whereas *partiinost'* is "subjective." The scientist, as a "subject" in search of the truth about an "object," has certain personal characteristics which are themselves "subjective" and which interact

---

[26]Rachkov, p. 114.
[27]Ibid., p. 124.
[28]Ibid., pp. 131, 129-32.

with his search for "objective truth." *Partiinost'* is one of the "subjective" qualities of the scientist and helps orient him toward the selection of relevant "objective" information. Since the acquisition of "objective truth" is considered to be in the best interests of society, it is essential that the scientist have the "correct *partiinyi* approach" to his research.[29]

Partiinost' includes the need for a "revolutionary-critical relationship toward reality."[30]

The principle of *partiinost'* demands devotion to the ideals of communism and an actively effective participation in their realization. To be *partiinyi* means to be irreconcilable to any form of oppression of one person by another [and] to the exploitation of a person's physical and spiritual potentials. Proletarian *partiinost'* signifies the defense of the basic political interests of workers (prole-tariat) and every possible assistance [in] the struggle for the liquidation of capitalism, the class-antagonistic society, and [in] the cleansing of social life. . . .[31]

Natural scientists and sociologists are told that they must be "irreconcilable" to "bourgeois distortions" in their respective fields. According to Alekseev and Il'in, *partiinost'* does not in any way limit the creativity of scientists, because (by definition) the interests of Communist ideology and science coincide in the search for objective truth.[32]

One of the sources reviewed earlier provides a good example of the formal acceptance of the outward manifestations of *partiinost'*. Throughout his essays, N. N. Semenov makes frequent references to the important role played by the Communist party in supporting scientific research. He attributes much of the success of Soviet science to Lenin's foresight in giving early institutional support to fundamental

---

[29]Alekseev and Il'in, pp. 29-34. Rachkov also refers to the relationship between *partiinost'* and science, op. cit., p. 72.

[30]Alekseev and Il'in, p. 65.

[31]Ibid., p. 64.

[32]Ibid., pp. 68-74.

research. In relating his personal experiences, Semenov
reminisces warmly about his early contacts with members of
the Communist party, and he concludes that *"partiinost'* is
a characteristic trait . . . of every Soviet man."[33] "The
party is in us . . . [and] the power of our party [is] inseparable from its people. . . ."[34]

From a different perspective, Zhores Medvedev has warned
of the dangers inherent in a system that combines elements of
partiinost' with a centralized administration of science. In
his study of Lysenko, Medvedev demonstrates how a person can
use the management and control of science to promote personal
career interests by feeding false information to political
leaders. A leadership that is concerned more with the rapid
application of science to solve production problems than with
the careful testing of new ideas is vulnerable to the acceptance of claims for scientific panacea. This vulnerability is
compounded by the political labeling of different viewpoints
as "bourgeois distortions," since this makes it difficult (or
impossible) to subject potentially false doctrines to the
regular processes of scientific evaluation.[35] Although the
combination of *partiinost'* and government administration of
science may make the Soviet system susceptible, such aber-
rations of "normal science" are not the intention of Soviet
leaders. On the contrary, they hope that the efficient
organization and management of science will provide accurate
and useful information, which will contribute positively to
economic and social progress.

---

[33]N. N. Semenov, *Nauka i obshchestvo* (Moscow, 1973),
p. 464.
[34]Ibid., p. 476. See also pp. 105, 322-27, 455, 468-71.
[35]Zhores Medvedev, *The Rise and Fall of T. D. Lysenko*,
trans. I. Michael Lerner (New York: Columbia University
Press, 1969), pp. 244-53.

V. Social Consequences of the Scientific-Technical Revolution

Theoretically, an improvement in the efficiency of the organization of science will raise the productivity of scientists and will facilitate the more rapid application of scientific knowledge in production. The combined processes of scientific development and its technical application in the twentieth century are referred to as the "scientific-technical revolution." Soviet scholars generally try to place this phenomenon in conceptual and historical perspective. They consider the very nature of the continual and rapid expansion of contemporary science and technology as essentially different from previous forms of scientific change. The scientific-technical revolution is looked upon as a cumulative process that resulted during the midtwentieth century in a "qualitative leap in the knowledge of nature and the use of its laws."[1] This radical transformation in the substance and pace of scientific progress is analyzed as part of the social-historical process of building the material-technical base of communism.

When Soviet scholars refer to science as a productive force contributing to the material-technical base of communism, they make two general assumptions. One is that scientific progress is a major factor in the international struggle between capitalism and socialism, and the second is that the goals of science are inherently consistent with those of communism. Consequently, the scientific-technical revolution is expected to have a more positive impact in socialist than in capitalist countries, thereby contributing to the "ultimate victory" of communism.

The role of science in the international competition for prestige and military power is often used to promote the

---

[1]A. Gusarov and V. Radaev, *Besedy po nauchno-tekhnicheskoi revoliutsii* (Moscow, 1972), p. 8.

the critical importance of *naukovedenie* in the Soviet Union.
Presumably the study of science will contribute to the government's use of science and technology and will strengthen
the Soviet position vis-à-vis the West. Science is seen as
another form of power held by the ruling class, and as such
it can be used for constructive or destructive purposes depending on the class in power at the time. According to
Marxism-Leninism, capitalists use science to exploit and
repress the masses; whereas in the Soviet Union science is
in the hands of the people and is used to benefit the whole
society.

The differences that are anticipated in the social
effects of scientific and technical change can be traced to
the Soviet theory of the contrasting economic structures of
capitalism and socialism. When science becomes a productive
force in capitalist economies, it exacerbates existing con-
tradictions; whereas in a socialist economy the productive
force of science facilitates the advancement of society
toward communism.

Although most of the Soviet sociologists of science do
not engage in ideological polemics, their references to the
relationship between science and society in the United States
are almost always negative. At the international level,
American political leaders are accused of using science for
aggressive militaristic purposes and for a policy of "technological colonialism."[2] Domestically, since the goals of
science are considered incompatible with those of capitalism,
scientific development is expected to increase the profits of
big business and to intensify class conflicts within society.
The pessimistic predictions of several American writers are
often used to buttress the Soviet argument that problems
such as technologically produced unemployment, alienation,
and mass conditioning are examples of the negative consequences of science and technology in the United States.[3]

Most of the literature under review focuses on two ways
in which the scientific-technical revolution influences

---

[2]P. A. Rachkov, *Naukovedenie: problemy, struktura,
elementy* (Moscow, 1974), p. 79.
[3]For example, see A. G. Chemeris, "Sootnoshenie sotsial'-
nogo i nauchno-tekhnicheskogo progressa," in *Nauchno-
tekhnicheskaia revoliutsiia i obshchestvennyi progress*, ed.
E. A. Arab-Ogly et al. (Moscow, 1969), pp. 37-39, 64-66.

Soviet society. One is through the changes it brings to the socioeconomic structure, and the other is the effect it has on culture. A. A. Zvorykin, a senior Soviet scholar whose publications deal frequently with the impact of science and technology on social change, places particular emphasis on the concept *tekhnika*, which refers to "the means of labor and the means of human activity in the system of social production and social life."[4] He defines the "scientific-technical revolution" as a form of technical progress in which there is a coincidence of deep qualitative transformations in science and technique and a transfer of the leading role to science.

The nature of work and human activities in the system of social production are the primary means through which people are oriented to science and nature. As a result of the scientific-technical revolution there is a rapid change in the form of labor and labor relations. Zvorykin presents a diagram (next page) to depict these relationships:[5] *Tekhnika* is placed in the center and is related directly to people, nature (materials and energy), and science in the top half of the diagram. Through a series of solid and broken lines Zvorykin distinguishes between the regular ties (solid lines) and those that have acquired special significance during the scientific-technical revolution. He then relates the whole set of interactions (especially science) to the lower half of the scheme, which includes economic, political, social (personal), and ideological relationships and their respective forms of organization.[6]

Zvorykin calls his analysis a "structural-functional" approach to the study of society. Its only resemblance to the Western conception of structural-functional analysis is the division of society into analytical systems of activity ("economic," "political," and so forth) that interact with

---

[4]A. A. Zvorykin, *Nauchno-tekhnicheskaia revoliutsiia i ee sotsial'nye posledstviia* (Moscow, 1967), p. 4.
[5]Ibid., p. 60.
[6]Ibid., p. 9. For a description of how other Soviet scholars have related the concept *tekhnika* to the scientific-technical revolution, see Julian Cooper, "The Scientific and Technical Revolution in Soviet Theory" (Paper prepared for the Conference on Technology and Communist Culture, August 1975).

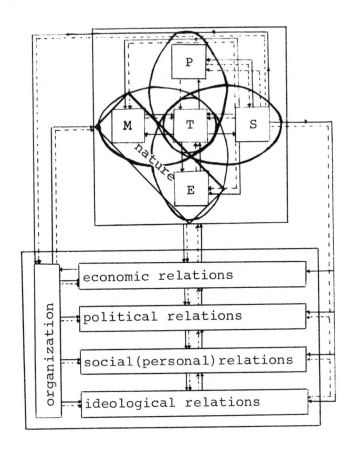

each other in some functional way. Since Zvorykin makes
tekhnika the focal point of his study, his attention is
centered on the impact that modern technology has had on
the organization of labor, especially the effects of automation on different spheres of employment, the specialization of labor, and the utilization of workers' time.

The problems of automation and the relationships between
people and machines are popular topics among Soviet science
specialists. In *The Sociology of Science*, for example, G. N.
Volkov discusses the ways that technology has led to the
partial replacement of human labor by machines. He maintains that mechanization and automation can be a threat or a
benefit to people depending on the circumstances.

84

Without much supporting evidence, however, Volkov suggests
that the danger of scientists' becoming subordinate to
machines is much greater in the industrial research process
of capitalism than under socialism.[7] E. A. Arab-Ogly tends
to agree with this view when he implies that "capitalist
man" uses the power of machines (during the industrial
revolution) and the power of computers (during the scientific-technical revolution) to manipulate, control, and
repress other people.[8] Ironically, this last point is the
mirror image of the view that several American scholars have
of the use of technology in the Soviet Union.

Arab-Ogly argues that under socialism human beings
remain the central productive force of society. Instead of
being displaced by machines, they are given new roles in
production, that is, from agents to "controllers" of production in the broad sense of the term, as forecast by Marx.[9]
This viewpoint is supported further by A. Gusarov and V.
Radaev, who assert that, although machines and technology
have been driving forces in the whole process of social
change, the essential role of mankind has not been destroyed.
Machines are the fulfillment of human knowledge and labor and
serve as the means for the transformation of human discoveries into life. Therefore the leading progressive force con-
tinues to be human beings, the carriers of scientific knowledge and productive experiences. Gusarov and Radaev conclude
that under socialism the issue is not people *or* machines;
rather, it is the cooperation of people *and* machines.[10]

Through their discussions of leisure time, several
Soviet analysts try to relate the transformations in the
nature and content of labor to personality development.
When automation leaves us with more nonworking hours, the
ways in which we spend our leisure time become more significant for the formation of attitudes and ideas. Arab-Ogly
contrasts the market orientation of leisure activities in

---

[7]G. N. Volkov, *Sotsiologiia nauki. Sotsiologicheskie
ocherki nauchno-tekhnicheskoi deiatel'nosti* (Moscow, 1968),
pp. 197, 206-7.
[8]E. A. Arab-Ogly, "O sotsial'nykh posledstviiakh
nauchno-tekhnicheskoi revoliutsii," in *Nauchno-tekhnicheskaia
revoliutsiia*, op. cit., pp. 8-11.
[9]Ibid., pp. 19-20.
[10]Gusarov and Radaev, pp. 105-8.

the West with what he considers to be the more constructive use of leisure time in the Soviet Union. While he offers no specific examples of how leisure contributes to personal fulfillment under communism, he implies that the transition from the "materialistic" motives of capitalism to the "moral" motives of communism (that is, its greater concern for personality building) represents a more advanced stage of human development.[11] In effect, Arab-Ogly is presenting the outlines of a theory regarding the changes in attitudes and values that occur under conditions of communism. Such a cultural transformation is regarded as an indirect result of scientific and technical progress.

The normative implications of scientific progress are addressed in greater detail by two Soviet scientists, N. N. Semenov and A. D. Sakharov. Semenov speaks of science as a great humanizing force whose purpose is to deliver all people from hunger and cold, and from the difficulties of physical labor. Science is expected to contribute also to a person's "spiritual-cognitive growth." Semenov is not referring to the penetration of scientific attitudes (for example, critical inquisitiveness) into a person's value system. By "spiritual" development he means the broadening of one's awareness of the world, that is, raising one's level of general education. This is done through the incorporation of scientific knowledge into the regular school system and the popularization of science through mass-oriented journals (for example, *Nauka i zhizn'*) and science societies (for example, *Znanie*).[12]

Semenov's exuberance and faith in the positive potential of science are evident in the way he describes the social application of scientific knowledge, although he does not believe that the beneficial consequences of science are inevitable. In 1961, for example, he outlined specific ways in which science and technology could be used to improve the living conditions and general well-being of mankind. Looking toward the future, he advocated the development and use of thermonuclear reactors, solar energy, and underground heat as three alternative sources of energy. Eleven years later, however, the problems of energy had worsened, and Semenov

---

[11]Arab-Ogly, pp. 10-11, 32-35.
[12]N. N. Semenov, *Nauka i obshchestvo* (Moscow, 1973), pp. pp. 6, 18, 169-71, et passim.

warned of the rapid depletion of the world's fuel supply. He argued that it was the responsibility of scientists and engineers to identify and study these problems, but their solutions were often limited by social institutions. On this and other occasions, Semenov blamed capitalism for obstructing the worldwide humanizing force of science.[13]

A different perspective is presented by the physicist A. D. Sakharov, who contends that as complex modern societies the Soviet Union and the United States have progressively similar social structures. In both systems it is the *human* factor that is the critical element in the application of scientific knowledge, so that the choice between socialism and capitalism will ultimately be a moral one, that is, which system will apply science to the fulfillment of basic human needs around the world?[14] Both scientists are relating science to humanistic goals, but they reach different conclusions concerning where and how these goals can be achieved.

Sakharov asks that the worldwide goal of preserving civilization be given higher priority than the ideological goal of preserving any one social system at the expense of others. He reminds us that science and technology have provided the means whereby problems of hunger and overpopulation can be alleviated, and he calls for economic and technical assistance to countries facing these crises. In his view, neither major power is responding adequately to such needs.[15] The human misuse (or nonuse) of science, therefore, goes beyond the ideological conflict between capitalism and socialism. Both systems are vulnerable to criticism. This is, perhaps, Sakharov's greatest point of departure from the official Soviet view.

The failure of governments to use science for the betterment of mankind is, according to Sakharov, "a threat to the independence and worth of the human personality, a

---

[13] Ibid., pp. 18-19, 28-33, 109-13, 149. However, he does not explain why greater energy conservation has not been developed in the Soviet Union.

[14] A. D. Sakharov, *Progress, Coexistence, and Intellectual Freedom* (New York: W. W. Norton and Co., Inc., 1968), pp. 71, 76.

[15] Ibid., pp. 44-47.

threat to the meaning of life."[16] He praises the "ethical character" of socialism for raising the meaning of labor and acting as a catalyst for social progress, but he warns that the surrounding dangers of war, poverty, and terror will prevent the free development of the human personality for most of mankind. He also foresees the negative implications of chemical and mechanical controls over life processes. Meanwhile, within the advanced societies, mass culture and authoritarian education combine to form another serious challenge to the integrity of the individual.[17] He does not want to stop scientific progress; he simply wants us to become more aware of the danger it poses to our value structure.

Sakharov also speaks of the "material" and "spiritual" consequences of the scientific-technical revolution, but he uses the terms differently from Arab-Ogly and Semenov. Materially, he says that science can destroy the world as we know it through a thermonuclear holocaust. Spiritually, science threatens the survival of individual and intellectual freedom. Sakharov says that "intellectual freedom is essential to human society."[18] This includes the "freedom to obtain and distribute information, freedom for open-minded and unfearing debate, and freedom from pressure by officialdom and prejudices."[19] When Sakharov advocates social adherence to these attitudes and conditions, he is, in effect, transferring some of the basic values of science into the social sphere. In this way, scientific attitudes would truly penetrate society and lead to a different kind of cultural revolution.

The views of other scientists were expressed in a survey conducted by *Literaturnaia gazeta* in 1971.[20] Prominent Soviet and non-Soviet scientists were asked their opinions on the social consequences of scientific research. Many of them responded by pointing to the negative implications of air pollution, genetic manipulation, and nuclear

---

[16] Ibid., p. 59.
[17] Ibid., pp. 59-61, et passim, 78.
[18] Ibid., p. 29.
[19] Ibid.
[20] M. Iaroshevsky, Iu. Sheinin, and B. Griaznov, "XX Vek. Nauka i obshchestvo," *Literaturnaia gazeta*, 19 September 1973, p. 11.

warfare. But they did not consider these problems to be rooted in science itself. According to Academician P. Aleksandrov, for example, "Science itself bears neither good nor evil. It places the means and the instruments in the hands of people, but how they will be used depends on the people themselves and the social structure."[21] Several other scientists disagreed and suggested that science itself was indeed becoming potentially more harmful.

Does this mean that some areas of research should be forbidden? The majority of scientists surveyed preferred to develop a stronger sense of awareness among scientists regarding the moral implications of their work, rather than to prohibit research arbitrarily on certain topics. In response to a question regarding the general impact of science on morality, it was argued that scientific reasoning develops a person's objectivity, and this has a positive effect on one's entire moral makeup. It was noted, however, that science is only one part of a complex set of social conditions that contribute to the moral character of scientists.

How does Soviet sociology deal with the relationship between science and morality? According to I. A. Maizel', A. Aleksandrov, and others, science assumes a moral dimension when knowledge becomes the basis for social behavior. Science helps to fulfill the human need for knowledge, that is, the transformation of the unknown into the known, into an intellectual mastery of the material and social environment. The predominant Soviet view is that once people know the objective laws of nature, they can predict the probability of certain behavior resulting from their actions. Science thereby enters the process of making rational decisions to obtain certain goals.[22] Assuming that their goals are morally "good" (and in Soviet ideology the goals of communism are defined as morally good), people would have a "scientific guide" to their subjective, moral initiatives. In other words, science develops human consciousness and enables subjective intentions to correspond with the results of one's actions. In this way, according to Soviet theory, science serves as a strong moral force.[23]

---

[21]Ibid.

[22]I. A. Maizel', *Nauka, avtomatizatsiia, obshchestvo* (Leningrad, 1972), pp. 269-73.

[23]A. Aleksandrov, "Nauka i nravstvennost'," *Izvestiia*, 12 March 1967, p. 5.

One of the many questions that arises from such an
analysis is whether the scientist, whose goal is the acquisition and development of knowledge, is responsible for the
social consequences of his research. The response given by
V. I. Tolstykh in his book *Science and Morality*[24] represents
a compromise between two prevailing points of view. Tolstykh
calls for a balance in responsibilities between scientists
and social institutions. He maintains that social obliga-
tions have always been part of the scientist's role and have
been particularly important since the scientific-technical
revolution of the twentieth century. The rapid penetration
of scientific achievements into our daily lives, the simul-
taneous capacity of science to destroy or save the world,
and the importance of science and technology in the "worldwide political struggle" make it impossible for the scientist to ignore the social consequences of his work.

Therefore, Tolstykh asks scientists not to pursue research that has potentially harmful results. While, in
principle, the "search for truth" requires the freedom to
explore all possible lines of inquiry, he suggests that in
practice the scientist should place certain limitations on
his own research. Nevertheless, the self-regulation of
scientists must be combined with a broader system of social
regulation. Scientists alone cannot be blamed for all the
social misfortunes that eventually develop from scientific
research because, as Tolstykh reminds us, ethical decisions
regarding the use of scientific discoveries become the
prerogative of those in power.[25]

We have come almost full circle, then, to the Soviet
view of the differences in the ways that political leaders
use science in capitalist and socialist countries. If,
according to Soviet theory, the social consequences of
science are different in the two types of systems, then the
responsibility of scientists must also be different. The
implication of the argument presented above is that it is
"moral" for the Soviet scientist to pursue most areas of
research, since he knows that the results will be used in
the interests of society. It is likewise "immoral" for
American scientists to pursue research which is destined to
benefit the ruling class. We may not agree with the

---

[24]V. I. Tolstykh, *Nauka i nravstvennost'* (Moscow, 1971).
[25]Ibid., p. 334.

ideological assumptions that lead to this conclusion; nevertheless, it is consistent with the Soviet interpretation of
the interaction of science with social systems and their
analysis of the historical context of scientific and technical change.

CONCLUSION

Sociology of Science as an Academic Field

The substantive focus of Soviet sociology of science, which distinguishes it from other academic fields, is the relationship between science and its social environment. The boundaries of the field are broadly defined, but they are drawn together by a common concern for science as a form of social activity. The literature is characterized by a diversity of topics and research techniques, most of which are interrelated and complementary. Yet each scholar brings a distinctive style and viewpoint to his or her work. Some are stronger in theoretical discussions; others rely more heavily on empirical data. Some focus on macrolevel analysis and others on microlevel research.

I. I. Leiman, for example, provides the conceptual basis for a sociological theory of science, and P. A. Rachkov presents a comprehensive and integrated analysis of science as a whole. By contrast, M. G. Iaroshevsky is concerned with the development of a microlevel theory of scientific creativity. G. M. Dobrov and his colleagues, who are more sophisticated in the analysis of empirical data, focus on the collection and processing of quantifiable information.

The combination of theory and data is an important step in the formation of a scientific discipline. Soviet sociologists approach the subject of science with common theoretical assumptions, which influence the nature and selection of research topics and provide the basic parameters for their analysis. With the notable exception of the work of Dobrov and a few others, the collection of data is usually not governed by explicit hypotheses. Most of the empirical research is problem-oriented and deals with middle-level analyses of particular research questions. (For example, what is the best "mix" of specialists in a scientific collective; what is the impact of age on creativity?)

Conclusions are drawn from the data and generalizations inferred within the original theoretical framework. The result is not a deductive scientific theory. Nevertheless, the findings of different researchers often substantiate one another, and there is a continual interaction of theory and data.

One way to gauge the development of an academic field is to look at its underlying concepts, generalizations, and theories. Despite the variety of topics and styles, there is a substantial consistency in the use of the concepts "science," "scientific collectives," and "science management." The generalizations that occur most frequently have been presented throughout this essay and many can be subsumed under the following: (1) socialism provides the most compatible form of social structure for the advancement of science; (2) science contributes to the material-technical base of communism; (3) improvements in the organization and management of science will increase scientific productivity; and (4) scientific creativity is a product of the interaction between social conditions, the psychological characteristics of the individual, and the logical development of science. These and more narrowly focused statements are interrelated by content and could be developed into a social theory of science.

The sociology of science is not as comprehensive as the entire field of *naukovedenie*. Its generalizations fall short of the interdisciplinary theory proposed by S. R. Mikulinsky and N. I. Rodny in 1966. Nevertheless, other academic perspectives have penetrated the sociological dimension of science through the varied backgrounds of individual scholars and the very nature of the subject matter. The social organization of science has been integrated with theories of management and communication systems. The sociology of scientific discovery is closely related to psychology and the philosophy of science. The social consequences of science bring in elements of normative theory. The result is that Soviet sociology of science is imbued with a multidisciplinary character, but not with an integrated empirical theory.

Soviet scholars have made great strides in the field since the Bernal-Mackay paper and the Lvov symposium in the mid-1960s. The systematic attention given to the social aspects of science has resulted in an improvement in the quality of theory and data available to the academic community. More significant, perhaps, is that the application of this research by the political leadership is expected to be directed toward the social control of science and the scientific control of society.

Social Control of Science

In a recent article on "Science Policy and Assessment in the Soviet Union," G. M. Dobrov states that the objective of *naukovedenie* is "to draw general theoretical conclusions from the experience gained in scientific and technological development in order to control this process more effectively by the use of social means of action."[1] Throughout the article Dobrov's emphasis is on science as "a controllable system." Most of the material reviewed in this essay could be reexamined in terms of its contribution to the social control of science.

As previously noted, one of the pervasive characteristics of the literature is its focus on the social environment of scientific research, which includes the immediate working situation of the scientific collective and the more encompassing system of social relations. Since, from the Marxian perspective, the scientist is an integral part of his environment, it is logical to expect that changes in surrounding conditions will affect the activities of the scientist himself. Soviet studies of the social organization of scientific research are based on this expectation. The manipulation of the scientist's social environment becomes the primary means through which leaders try to control the scientist's behavior.

While it is true that some aspects of science are vulnerable to social manipulation, there are inherent impediments to the imposition of total control. As a social system, scientists are integrated through their role structure and professional ethics. They constitute a group of scholars who have vested interests in the pursuit of science and in the maintenance of their professional status. The controllers of science have to penetrate the scientific community with social norms and political goals that are congenial to the

---

[1]Gennady M. Dobrov, "Science Policy and Assessment in the Soviet Union," *International Social Science Journal*, no. 3 (1973), p. 306.

94

norms and goals of scientists. Soviet sociologists minimize
this problem by asserting that socialism and *partiinost'* are
compatible with science, but the assertion and the reality
are not necessarily the same.

Naukovedenie specialists recognize a different limitation, namely the role of individual personalities in particular discoveries. Perhaps it is possible that social-psychological research will uncover the environmental factors most
conducive to scientific creativity; ideal forms of "think
tanks" might be established to promote the "explosions of
genius" that will move science forward. Nonetheless, controls over the social environment do not guarantee a regulation of the substantive output of science. As the studies
of Iaroshevsky and others demonstrate, the personal characteristics of the scientist play a crucial role in the perception and development of new ideas. One's personality may
be influenced by lifetime experiences and surrounding social
conditions, but the idiosyncratic nature of the individual
scientist is both a necessary ingredient to scientific growth
and an obstacle to total social control of science.

The nature of science as a system of knowledge is a
further impediment to its social regulation. While admit-
ting that mankind is limited by the current level of accumulated knowledge, Soviet writers suggest that an understanding
of the inner logic of scientific development will enable us
to identify those areas and methods of inquiry that bear the
greatest promise for the future advancement of science. This
may be true in a general sense for short-term planning, but
there are inherent limitations to extrapolations from previous and current knowledge. It may be evident, for example,
that new ideas are needed in certain areas of science, but
the particular form of scientific discoveries cannot be pre-
dicted and controlled in advance. Furthermore, with regard
to fundamental changes in scientific perspectives, the precise nature and content of a scientific revolution cannot be
foreseen until the paradigm shift actually occurs.

The professionalism of science, the psychological aspects of scientific discovery, and the logical development
of scientific knowledge are three limitations to the social
control of science.   In addition, there are myriad administrative problems associated with the coordination of a
huge network of scientific institutions and the application
of science to production. The rapid pace of scientific and

technological growth has further exacerbated the difficulties of processing the output of science and maintaining
effective channels of communication among scientists. Improvements in the nature and procedures of science management have been recognized, therefore, as a vital part of
Soviet science policy.

The sociology of science is part of the informational
input that, under ideal circumstances, allows the government
to make "rational" decisions with regard to science policy.
The rationality of the decision assumes the accuracy of the
information and its applicability to desired goals. The
immediate goal of science management, in the limited sense
of improving the organization and efficiency of scientific
research, is only a part of the broader economic and political objectives of *naukovedenie*. Dobrov says that the general purpose of science management is

> to make effective use of available scientific
> resources and achievements and to build up
> scientific potential on a scale consonant with
> the future requirements of society and in ac-
> cordance with a scientifically forecast strategy
> of scientific activity.[2]

Beyond this are the goals of raising the technological level
of society and the creation of a cultural transformation
throughout the Soviet Union.

Scientific Control of Society

The application of the sociology of science is expected
to contribute also to science management in its broader
sense, that is, the use of science and technology for social
control. Dobrov addresses this point when he says, "The
social assessment of science will, in the foreseeable future,
become an inseparable and important part of the scientifically based management of the social development of society."[3]
Science, itself a social system with its own normative
structure, has a cumulative impact on the values of society
as a whole. During the process of social development, it is
expected that science and technology will continue to change

---

[2]Ibid., p. 316.
[3]Ibid., p. 325.

the nature and meaning of work, living habits, human perceptions and expectations. The implication of Dobrov's statement is that scientific knowledge can be applied to manage this process and to direct it toward the completion of communism in the USSR. This presumes that the social effects of science are manageable and that human behavior is amenable to systematic social control.

In *The Scientific Management of Society* V. G. Afanas'ev shows how the natural and social sciences contribute to the direction and control of Communist society.

'The construction of communism is based on science.' . . . The development of the social sciences and practical application of their recommendations are no less important to material production and spiritual progress than [the] utilisation of achievements [in] the natural sciences. . . . Society can be scientifically directed in its progress from socialism to communism only on the basis of exact knowledge of the processes involved.[4]

Afanas'ev's analysis of social behavior is a combination of Marxism and cybernetics. He defines control in terms of the information systems that regulate human activities, the ultimate purpose of which is "to optimize the system's functioning."[5] The crucial questions, of course, are "Who will be the controllers of the information and who decides what constitutes the 'optimum' functioning of the system?" Afanas'ev's answer, consistent with Marxism-Leninism, is that communism will be a self-regulating system, and people will control themselves.[6] Western scholars would be quick to point out the discrepancies between Afanas'ev's theory and the reality of Soviet life. The important thing is not

_____

[4]V. G. Afanasyev (*sic*), *The Scientific Management of Society* (Moscow, 1971), p. 5. Afanas'ev's quote is from the CPSU Central Committee (Theses), *50th Anniversary of the Great October Revolution* (Moscow, 1967), p. 29.

[5]Afanasyev (*sic*), p. 23, italicized in source.

[6]Actually Afanas'ev views capitalist society also as an "integral self-controlling system." The difference is that under capitalism the bourgeoisie are in control of the major social processes. Ibid., p. 40.

that Afanas'ev's theory does not correspond with current
reality, but that attempts are being made to develop and
apply such a theory in the future.

The data gathered by social theorists are thought to
be essential for the "scientific management of society."
Assuming that the information is accurate and that it can be
interpreted and processed effectively by political leaders,
then it would only be a matter of time, theoretically, before
social and political regulation become complete. The systematic control of human bahavior may be a frightening prospect
to those who maintain different ideological perspectives.
Others may feel secure in the belief that such control is
not possible. Certainly, the assumptions of accurate data
and effective processing may not be realistic, thereby leading to a breakdown of the theory in practice. Nevertheless,
Soviet theorists regard greater social control as both possible and desirable, and much of their research on the
sociology of science is directed toward this end.

SELECTED BIBLIOGRAPHY

The bibliography does not include all the sources reviewed for this study nor all the ones referred to in footnotes. It is a selective listing of the materials that are most useful and most representative of the subjects discussed. More extensive bibliographies can be found in many of the books on the list.

Academy of Sciences of the USSR. *Institute of History of Science and Technology.* 1971.

Afanas'ev, V. G. *Nauchno-tekhnicheskaia revoliutsiia, upravlenie, obrazovanie.* Moscow, 1972.

_____. *The Scientific Management of Society.* Moscow, 1971.

Aleksandrov, A. "Nauka i nravstvennost'." *Izvestiia.* 12 March 1967.

Alekseev, P. V. and Il'in, A. Ia. *Printsip partiinosti i estestvoznanie.* Moscow, 1972.

Arab-Ogly, E. A. et al. *Nauchno-tekhnicheskaia revoliutsiia i obshchestvennyi progress.* Moscow, 1969.

Barykina, O. A. "Bibliografiia naukovedeniia v SSSR." *Voprosy istorii estestvoznaniia i tekhniki,* nos. 47-48 (1974), pp. 142-44.

Beliaev, E. A., Mikulinsky, S. R., and Sheinin, Iu. M., eds. *Organizatsiia nauchnoi deiatel'nosti.* Moscow, 1968.

Bernal, J. D. and Mackay, A. L. "Na putiakh k nauke o nauke." *Voprosy istorii estestvoznaniia i tekhniki,* no. 21 (1967), pp. 62-68.

Bibler, V. S., Griaznov, B. S., and Mikulinsky, S. R., eds. *Ocherki istorii i teorii razvitiia nauki.* Moscow, 1969.

"Chelovek-nauka-tekhnika." *Voprosy filosofii,* no. 6 (1972), pp. 184-85, and no. 8 (1972), pp. 29-40.

Chinakal, N. A., ed. *Organizatsiia i effektivnost' nauchnykh issledovanii.* Novosibirsk, 1965 (reissued in 1967).

_____, ed. *Puti povysheniia effektivnosti nauchnogo truda.* Novosibirsk, 1966.

"Chlen-korr. AN SSSR S. R. Mikulinsky, zam. direktora
Instituta istorii estestvoznaniia i tekhniki AN SSSR."
Voprosy filosofii, no. 1 (1972), pp. 156-58.
Davydov, A. G. "Sotsial'nye problemy organizatsii nauki i
truda uchenykh pri sotsializme." Dissertation for the
Candidate Degree. Ural State University, 1972.
Dobrov, G. M. *Nauka o nauke*. Kiev, 1966. 2d ed., 1970.
_____. "Science Policy and Assessment in the Soviet Union."
International Social Science Journal, no. 3 (1973),
pp. 305-25.
_____, Klimeniuk, V. N., Odrin, V. M., and Savel'ev, A. A.
Organizatsiia nauki. Kiev, 1970.
Dzhelomanova, G. P., Meleshchenko, Iu. S., and Kugel', S. A.,
eds. *Problemy deiatel'nosti uchenogo i nauchnykh
kollektivov*. Vols. I-V. Leningrad, 1968-73.
Gurgenidze, Gennady. "Problems of the Science of Science: A
Survey." *Social Sciences*, no. 1 (1974), pp. 73-77.
Gusarov, A., and Radaev, V. *Besedy po nauchno-tekhnicheskoi
revoliutsii*. Moscow, 1972.
Gvishiani, D. M., ed. *Upravlenie, planirovanie, i organizatsiia nauchnykh i tekhnicheskikh issledovanii*. Vols.
I-V. Moscow, 1970.
_____, Mikulinsky, S. R., and Kugel', S. A., eds. *Nauchno-
tekhnicheskaia revoliutsiia i izmenenie struktury
nauchnykh kadrov SSSR*. Moscow, 1973.
_____ and Zvorykin, A. A., eds. *Osnovnye printsipy i
obshchie problemy upravleniia naukoi*. Moscow, 1973.
_____ and _____, eds. *Sotsial'no-ekonomicheskie i
organizatsionnye voprosy nauki v SSSR*. Vols. I-IV.
Moscow, 1970.
Iaroshevsky, M. G., ed. *Chelovek nauki*. Moscow, 1974.
_____, ed. *Sotsial'no-psikhologicheskie problemy nauki:
uchenyi i nauchnyi kollektiv*. Moscow, 1973.
_____, Sheinin, Iu., and Griaznov, B. "XX Vek. Nauka i
obshchestvo." *Literaturnaia gazeta*. 19 September 1973.
(See also Yaroshevsky, Mikhail.)
Karpov, M. M. *Nauka i razvitie obshchestva*. Moscow, 1961.
_____. *Sotsiologiia nauki*. Rostov-na-Donu, 1968.
Kedrov, B. M. "Puti razvitiia nauki i tekhniki." *Voprosy
istorii estestvoznaniia i tekhniki*, nos. 36-37 (1971-
72), pp. 3-7.
_____. "Regarding the Laws of the Development of Science."
Social Sciences, no. 1 (1974), pp. 26-45.
Kelle, V. Zh. and Mikulinsky, S. R., eds. *Sotsiologicheskie
problemy nauki*. Moscow, 1974.

Klimeniuk, V. N. *Upravlenie razvitiem i ispol'zovaniem nauchnogo potentsiala.* Kiev, 1974.

Kosolapov, V. V., and Shcherban', A. N. *Optimizatsiia nauchno-issledovatel'skoi deiatel'nosti.* Kiev, 1971.

Kugel', S. A. *Novoe v izuchenii sotsial'noi struktury obshchestva.* Leningrad, 1968.

_____, Lebin, B. D., and Meleshchenko, Iu. S., eds. *Nauchnye kadry Leningrada.* Leningrad, 1973.

Kurakov, I. G. *Nauka, tekhnika i voprosy stroitel'stva kommunizma.* Translated by Carin Dedijer. Oxford: Pergamon Press, 1966.

Leiman, I. I. *Nauka kak sotsial'nyi institut.* Leningrad, 1971.

Maizel', I. A. *Nauka, avtomatizatsiia, obshchestvo.* Leningrad, 1972.

_____. *Sotsiologiia nauki: problemy i perspektivy.* Leningrad, 1974.

_____ and Plotkin, S. Ia. "Problemy kompleksnogo izucheniia razvitiia nauki." *Voprosy istorii estestvoznaniia i tekhniki,* no. 21 (1967), pp. 69-77.

Medvedev, Zhores. *The Medvedev Papers.* Translated by Vera Rich. London: Macmillan London Ltd., 1971.

_____. *The Rise and Fall of T. D. Lysenko.* Translated by I. Michael Lerner. New York: Columbia University Press, 1969.

Mezhuev, V. M. "Nauka v sovremennoi kul'ture." *Voprosy filosofii,* no. 1 (1972), pp. 56-67.

Mikulinsky, S. R. "Naukovedenie: problemy i issledovaniia 70-kh godov." *Voprosy filosofii,* no. 7 (1975), pp. 40-52.

Mikulinsky, Semyon (*sic*). "The Science of Science as a General Theory of the Development of Science." *Social Sciences,* no. 1 (1974), pp. 46-57.

Mikulinsky, S. R., and Iaroshevsky, M. G., eds. *Nauchnoe otkrytie i ego vospriiatie.* Moscow, 1971.

_____ and _____, eds. *Nauchnoe tvorchestvo.* Moscow, 1969.

_____ and _____. "Sotsial'no-psikhologicheskie aspekty nauchnoi deiatel'nosti." *Voprosy filosofii,* no. 1 (1973), pp. 27-37.

_____ and Rodny, N. I. "Nauka kak predmet spetsial'nogo issledovaniia." *Voprosy filosofii,* no. 5 (1966), pp. 25-38.

_____ and Yaroshevsky (*sic*), M. G. "Apperception of a Scientific Discovery as a Problem of the Science of Science." Translated by Maria Hoser. *Zagadnienia naukoznawstwa* (1970), pp. 65-78.

Mirskaia, E. Z. "Eticheskie reguliativy funktsionirovaniia nauki." *Voprosy filosofii*, no. 3 (1975), pp. 131-38.
_____. "Nauchnaia deiatel'nost' uchenogo kak sotsial'no obuslovlennyi protsess." Disseration for the Candidate Degree. Rostov State University, 1968.
Mogilev, A. I., ed. *Chelovek-nauka-tekhnika*. Moscow, 1973.
Prikhod'ko, P. T. *Puti v nauku*. Moscow, 1973.
Rabkine, Yakov. "Origines et développements de la recherche sur la recherche en Union Soviétique." *Le Progrès scientifique*, no. 170 (1974), pp. 39-51.
Rachkov, P. A. *Naukovedenie: problemy, struktura, elementy*. Moscow, 1974.
Rodny, N. I. "Istoriia nauki, naukovedenie, nauka." *Voprosy filosofii*, no. 5 (1972), pp. 51-62.
Sakharov, A. D. *Progress, Coexistence, and Intellectual Freedom*. New York: W. W. Norton & Company, Inc., 1968.
Semenov, N. N. *Nauka i obshchestvo*. Moscow, 1973.
Sergeeva, I. V. "Kollektiv i lichnost' v nauke." *Sotsial'-nye issledovaniia*, no. 3 (1970), pp. 178-88.
_____. "Sotsial'nye problemy organizatsii nauchnogo tvorchestva." Dissertation for the Candidate Degree. Institute of Concrete Social Research, USSR Academy of Sciences, 1970.
Sichivitsa, O. M. *Mobil'nost' nauki*. Gorky, 1975.
Tolstykh, V. I. *Nauka i nravstvennost'*. Moscow, 1971.
Trapeznikov, S., et al. *Nauchno-tekhnicheskaia revoliutsiia i sotsial'nyi progress*. Moscow, 1972.
Volkov, G. N. "Izmenenie sotsial'noi orientatsii nauki." *Voprosy filosofii*, no. 1 (1969), pp. 35-46.
_____. *Sotsiologiia nauki. Sotsiologicheskie ocherki nauchno-tekhnicheskoi deiatel'nosti*. Moscow, 1968.
Yaroshevsky (*sic*), Mikhail. "The External and Inner Motivation of Scientific Creativity." *Social Sciences*, no. 1 (1974), pp. 58-72.
Zavlin, P. N., Shcherbakov, A. I., and Iudelevich, M. A. *Trud v sfere nauki*. 2d ed. Moscow, 1973.
Zvorykin, A. A. *Nauchno-tekhnicheskaia revoliutsiia i ee sotsial'nye posledstviia*. Moscow, 1967.
_____ and Kissel', E. I., eds. *Otsenka deiatel'nosti nauchnykh i inzhenerno-tekhnicheskikh rabotnikov i uluchshenie ikh ispol'zovaniia*. Moscow, 1973.